THE COMPLETE BOOK OF

BEAUTY

Avon Books are available at special quantity discounts for bulk purchases for sales promotions, premiums, fundraising or educational use. Special books, or book excerpts, can also be created to fit specific needs.

For details write or telephone the office of the Director of Special Markets, Avon Books, Dept. FP, 1350 Avenue of the Americas, New York, New York 10019, 1-800-238-0658.

THE COMPLETE BOOK OF

BEAUTY

VIKTOR BLEVI and GRETCHEN SWEEN

Illustrated by
Sandra Rediger

AVON BOOKS ◆ NEW YORK

THE COMPLETE BOOK OF BEAUTY is an original publication of Avon Books. This
work has never before appeared in book form.

AVON BOOKS
A division of
The Hearst Corporation
1350 Avenue of the Americas
New York, New York 10019

First Avon Books Trade Printing: May 1993

AVON TRADEMARK REG. U.S. PAT. OFF. AND IN OTHER COUNTRIES, MARCA REGISTRADA,
HECHO EN U.S.A.

Printed in the U.S.A.

OPM   10 9 8 7 6 5 4 3 2 1

THE COMPLETE BOOK OF
BEAUTY

Introduction

This book is all about beauty—not only how to acquire it but also what it is and why it is. *The Complete Book of Beauty* is a natural companion for the woman or man who knows there is more to beauty than meets the eye.

Containing extensive information, *The Complete Book of Beauty* is a comprehensive, convenient reference source on a subject of interest to almost everyone. Entries are alphabetically arranged, giving information on everything from product ingredients to people famed throughout history for their beauty, from specific beauty and health care issues to the cultural myths about beauty.

In *The Complete Book of Beauty*, beauty is observed, interpreted, and described from an eclectic range of perspectives: the historical, philosophical, anthropological, literary, scientific, and, of course, the aesthetic.

No book will ever demystify the enchanting spell of a beautiful person, just as no scientist, philosopher, or artist will discover the formula for the perfect face. Beauty is as elusive as it is multiformed; its infinite varieties defy generalizations. *The Complete Book of Beauty* is intended to inform and deepen our appreciation of human beauty in all its forms.

—Viktor Blevi and Gretchen Sween

Accessories

*"Know, first, who you are; and then
adorn yourself accordingly"*
—Epictetus, *Discourses*

The use of accessories marks a critical movement beyond mere utility and protection in the history of human adornment. However, this innovation did not follow far behind the basic demands of warmth and protection. Accessorizing has been a central part of personal beautification nearly as long as humans have been adorning themselves.

Accessories, past and present, are derived from teeth, horn, bones, rare stones and jewels, fresh flowers, glossy shells, feathers, beads, animal hides, pounded metals, and special fabrics. These materials are or have been employed as belts, earrings, bracelets, anklets, rings, necklaces, headdresses, and more.

Accessories serve numerous functions. Aside from beautifying existing garments, accessories are used to heighten or symbolize erogenous body parts. For instance, the bustle was used in the nineteenth century to emphasize a woman's derriere and medieval codpieces were sewn on men's pants to accentuate their virility. Many accessories, especially jewelry, are worn for their intrinsic value or as status symbol; Levi's jeans serve the latter function for contemporary Russians as do Rolex watches for many Americans.

Most important, the wearing of accessories constitutes a complex act of symbolic communication. In traditional cultures (and even among us supposedly civilized folks), accessories are worn to ward off evil spirits or to bring good luck. In African tribes, colored beads are worn to appease angry ancestor spirits, some Islamic and Mediterranean people encourage the wearing of veils as a protection from the "evil eye," Europeans in the Middle Ages wore strings of garlic around their necks

2

"to ward off witches," and many modern Westerners wear crucifixes not only as jewelry but also as a kind of lucky charm.

Throughout history, accessories have been a means for marking age, social standing, life-style, ceremonial or sacred occasions, group identity, power, and authority. The headdress of an Indian chief and an American military general's decorations are remarkably similar. Virtually all religious groups create special ritual garments for participants; for example, consider the Jewish prayer shawl, the Catholic pope's elaborate crown and gown, and the animal masks and trinkets of the tribal shaman. The Mendi in Africa wear special mourning beads in times of grief. Zulu girls wear beaded love messages around their necks. Students around the world are identifiable by their backpacks, just as judges are by their robes of state. Mongolian women wear elaborate headdresses, just as American men and women wear bands on the ring finger of the left hand to indicate married status. Accessories play an important part in the expression of individuality or rebellion—for example, Michael Jackson's glove or a punk rocker's safety pin jewelry.

Although the local manifestations differ widely, all people rely on accessories to communicate many things about their culture as well as their individual values, preferences, fears, and sources of pride. Ornamental baubles unite members of a group, and they enable individuals to stand out. With accessories, personal beauty is made and enhanced, and the human body is transformed into an important site for creative, ritualistic experimentation.

See also: FASHION, TATTOOS

Acid-alkaline Balance

See: pH BALANCE

Acne

Acne is most commonly associated with puberty. However, for some people it remains a lifelong problem.

During puberty, the secretion of the oil glands in the skin is increased by the changing activity of other glands. This increased oiliness, combined with negligent hygiene, can clog the skin's pores and lead to pimples. In addition, sebaceous glands secrete a greasy semiliquid called sebum. When these glands are congested, they dilate, and a threadlike substance develops. The outer end of the thread emerges through the skin's pores, showing a dark discoloration. These blemishes are called comedones, more commonly known as blackheads. *Comedo* is the Latin word for "glutton." Blackheads often plague the complexion of the over indulgent voluptuary. However, comedones (blackheads) do not become pimples, also known as whiteheads, until they are invaded by streptococci, a type of bacteria.

Heredity determines skin type, as well as all physical attributes, and, therefore, has something to do with the probability of developing acne. Blacks and other dark-skinned persons are less likely to experience severe cases of acne, but because of the delicacy of black skin, severe cases are more likely to leave raised scars. Dark skin is naturally more oily than fair skin; however, the application of strong astringents can dry out the skin and turn it an ashen color (called hypopigmentation). The natural glow from oil characteristic of black skin actually indicates a health advantage that manufacturers have tried to capture in producing cosmetic foundations for fair skin. Black skin retains moisture more readily and is less susceptible to sun-related damage.

Curing Acne. Applying harsh astringents like pure rubbing alcohol does not eliminate acne. Harsh astringents and soaps dry the skin too thoroughly, and the oil glands begin working more energetically to compensate. Washing the face too frequently is not beneficial either. If the essential protective coating of oil is utterly removed from the surface of the skin, bacteria breed, generating more acne. To help protect the skin after washing the face with hot water, rinse with cold water so that the pores will close again. An acne treatment mentioned in the Papyrus Ebers, composed in 1500 B.C., involves the use of an abrasive scrub made from alabaster and grain. Up until World War I, an even harsher treatment with dental burrs and rasps was about the only recommended treatment. Dermatologists (skin specialists) now use highly developed electric scrapers for removing acne without devastating the tender skin below. Blackheads may be removed with a *comedo extractor*. This tool is also sold in surgical supply stores and some drugstores, so it may be used at home. A comedo extractor lessens the potential for the scarring that can occur when blackheads are squeezed or picked with the fingers. However, when blackheads become infected and develop into red bumps (pimples), the comedo extractor can cause further harm. Treat pimples with medicated lotions or creams. If pimples are either completely ignored or unwisely aggravated, cysts and scars can develop. Physicians can prescribe antibiotic gels and oral medications to meet specific needs in more serious cases.

See also: ALCOHOL, SKIN, SOAP

How to Avoid Acne

- Keep hair clean to avoid oil buildup on forehead.
- Wear light, nonoil-based makeup.
- Clean hands before touching the face.
- Use moisturizers after washing the face.
- Avoid eating saturated fats (whole milk, butter, margarine, shortenings, cheese, chocolate), especially if prone to food allergies.

Adonis

> *"The field's chief flower, sweet above compare,*
> *Stain to all nymphs,*
> *more lovely than a man,*
> *More white and red than doves or roses are;*
> *Nature that made thee, with herself at strife,*
> *Saith that the world hath ending with thy life."*
> —Shakespeare, Venus and Adonis

Adonis is the Greek god most associated with masculine beauty. The origins of his persona are linked to ancient Semitic culture. Adonis was a noble hunter and protector of the harvest, a symbol of regeneration and fertility, and he was especially concerned that the flowers blossom brilliantly in the spring.

Complex relationships between beauty, sexuality, innocence, and mortality move through the Adonis myth. Aphrodite, the goddess of love, fell passionately in love with him and agonized over his violent death and castration by a wild boar, a fate she sadly witnessed. According to Greek myth, Aphrodite's love for the youth was so strong that she was able to rescue him from the underworld for a portion of each year. The characterization of Adonis as a "boy-god" indifferent to love (Aphrodite's in particular) became part of the myth much later. This is how he is depicted in Shakespeare's long narrative poem entitled Venus and Adonis. (Venus is the Roman name for Aphrodite.)

In the older myths Adonis was a profoundly spiritual as well as sexually innocent figure, and the parallels between Adonis and Jesus

Christ, the Christian savior, are unmistakable. Both claim Bethlehem as a birthplace. Adonis's mother is the virgin Myrrha of the sea; Jesus's mother is the Virgin Mary. Like Christ, Adonis was sacrificed at Easter time. Adonis was castrated as part of his death and Christ was crucified; both of these acts were symbols of a loss of worldly power in their respective cultures, the Greek and the Roman. Following this utterly debasing death, both were afforded transcendence to a loftier place: Adonis in the sea, and Christ in heaven. Although the early religious significance of Adonis has lost common currency, his name continues to be a synonym for any especially handsome man.

See also: APHRODITE

Aging

> *"As a white candle*
> *In a holy place,*
> *So is the beauty*
> *Of an aged face."*
> —Joseph Campbell, "The Old Woman"

Frequently, there is a relationship in mammals between body size and longevity. For example, elephants lead exceedingly long lives and cats relatively short ones. In proportion to body size, human beings have an abnormally long life span (74.7 years in the United States, 69.6 in the former Soviet Union). This is a result of the complexity of the human brain, which affords humans the ability to alter their environment, even to the point of mastering microscopic organisms that cause fatal diseases. In this century alone, life expectancy has nearly doubled in the United States, with a dramatic rise in the last two decades. Some researchers believe that in the near future the average life expectancy will be 100 years.

Ironically for such a long-lived species, humans tend to believe a youthful appearance is the most beautiful. This standard of beauty is not only arguable but even damaging, for no one can look nineteen forever. However, vibrancy and good health can allow beauty to continue well into maturity.

The Aging Process. It is an indisputable fact that the body changes with age. As time passes, the process of mitosis, or cell reproduction, slows. Many cells die out, and some, like brain cells, are never replaced. As we age we gradually lose height, hair, elasticity in the skin, the ability to retain heat, tactile sensitivity, teeth, hearing, sight, and sense of smell, among other things. After age forty, the back begins to bend forward. But as soon as age twenty, metabolism begins to slow about 3 percent every decade, which can lead to "middle-age spread" unless appropriate adjustments in diet and exercise are made. While the body is mostly preoccupied with losing things as time progresses, oddly, cartilage is one of the few tissues that continues to develop. Therefore, the nose and ears, which are largely composed of cartilage, may actually grow. The speed of tooth decay decreases as enamel hardens, but gum disease increases. With age, the heart pumps less blood, so smoking, a high cholesterol diet, and sedentary life-style become even greater risks later in life.

The most obvious signs of age appear on the skin. The skin begins to dry out (a process accelerated by exposure to the sun), lose elasticity, and sag. The sagging effect is what we call wrinkles. Age spots form when the production of pigmentation becomes irregular, another inevitability.

Extending Youth. People do not age overnight. It is important to remember that aging is part of an inevitable biological process that begins at birth and ends in death. This is a fact no one has ever managed to escape. Neither has anyone ever successfully managed to turn the clock back—although myth and legend about such phenomena abound; at present, thirteen Americans are frozen in hopes of someday being brought back to life. All sorts of odd procedures have been attempted in hopes of fooling nature: Pope Innocent VII drank the blood of young donors; Winston Churchill, Charlie Chaplin, and Christian Dior received injections of fetal lamb tissue; and many people have tried excessive doses of vitamins. Scientists are currently experimenting with several hormonal treatments that appear to slow the aging process in animals. But evidence demonstrates that for the time being the only means for delaying or softening the effects of aging are regular exercise, lifelong conscientious attention to nutrition, and unabated mental activity.

According to a statistical index compiled by *Harper's* magazine in 1987, 66 percent of all Americans claim to feel younger than their age. The power of mind over matter is quite real. Beauty in advancing age is neither impossible nor exceptional. It is usually the reward for a lifetime of discipline, self-respect, and communal interaction. The specific beauty of youth is inappropriate in an older face, but a youthful spirit is not.

Alcohol

"Alcohol" is the word used to describe a class of organic compounds. The word comes from Arabic *al* (a particle) and *kohl* (the name of a powder used in the East as eye makeup). Ethyl alcohol is a colorless, volatile, inflammable fluid that is the intoxicating agent in fermented beverages. This same substance has great solvent properties, which is why it is used in so many cosmetic and medicinal products.

Alcohol is produced through the fermentation of grain, starch (potatoes, corn, etc.), or sugar. It works as an antiseptic on the skin, reduces perspiration, and cools the skin as it evaporates. When alcohol is rubbed thoroughly into the skin it cause tissues to contract, blood vessels to dilate, and the result is a minor counterirritant effect. Rubbing alcohol, which is designated for external use only, is actually 70 percent denatured ethyl alcohol and 30 percent isopropanol. Because of its drying power, alcohol (in any form) should be used sparingly, especially on dry skin, the scalp, and the hair. Cosmetics that contain a significant amount of alcohol (like hair gel, hair spray, and skin toners) should be used sparingly.

The consumption of alcoholic beverages should remain moderate if one is to keep healthy skin. Long-term and extensive alcohol consumption leads to permanent dilation of the blood vessels, giving skin a saggy, weathered, and unnaturally flushed appearance. Alcohol is among the most caloric and nonnutritious beverages people consume. Many relatively minor health and beauty concerns, such as water retention, chronic fatigue, and a poor complexion, can be traced to habitual alcohol consumption. Furthermore, alcoholism is associated with several serious health conditions, such as cirrhosis of the liver, diabetes, and high blood pressure.

Allergens

Allergens are substances known to cause an allergic reaction. Some people are especially inclined to allergic reactions, but allergies may develop in anyone at any stage in life. Common allergic reactions to cosmetic products are skin irritation or itchy, irritated eyes.

For every substance that exists on the planet, somewhere there is an individual who is allergic to it. However, many cosmetic manufacturers have developed products especially for sensitive, allergy-prone skin. The consumer who knows her or his particular allergies should, of course, read all cosmetic labels carefully before purchasing products. People susceptible to allergies, or who suspect that they might be sensitive to a particular product, should try a patch test before using a product regularly. Most department stores and even some drugstores display samples of products that can be tested before a purchase is made. A person with serious allergies should consult an allergist. Comprehensive testing for allergies is expensive, stressful, and time consuming, but the information it yields allows a doctor to prescribe a personalized preventive program. This ultimately means greater freedom for the consumer.

Contact dermatitis is an allergic reaction that can be caused by cosmetic products, among other substances. According to the Federal Food and Drug Administration, the highest rate of allergic reactions are caused by deodorants and antiperspirants, hair sprays, hair coloring products, bubble bath, mascara, moisturizers, eye creams, and chemical depilatories. In colonial times, women often suffered from what we can now identify as severe allergic reactions; many died from lead poisoning since lead was thought to be a perfectly acceptable ingredient in face and body powder. Today, the FDA carefully monitors the manufacture of cosmetic products to insure consumer safety. Increased technology and consumer awareness have engendered a heightened sense of responsibility on the part of cosmetic manufacturers to respond to the needs of allergy-prone consumers.

See also: COSMETICS, HYPOALLERGENIC

Aloe Vera

Aloe vera is a member of the lily family. Its medicinal properties have long been recognized by numerous cultures, and recently the cosmetic and natural health care industries have begun to exploit the remarkably versatile properties of this plant. There is much evidence to support the aloe vera plant's reputation as a quick, natural remedy for minor skin disorders and an organic wrinkle preventer. The juice may be applied directly to the skin as a poultice for inflammation and second degree burns, such as sunburn.

Cleopatra, the legend of whose beauty has endured for more than two thousand years, used the juice of a plant that fits the description of aloe vera as a cream to protect her skin from the harsh Mediterranean sun. Perhaps she knew what we have only just rediscovered: that aloe vera naturally heals and protects damaged skin.

Aloe Vera

American Indians

The American Indians were the first contributors to the cosmetic "industry" in the New World. To protect against insects and harsh weather, they applied a primitive form of "cold cream" composed of animal fat. As its use evolved to that of a foundation for ceremonial paints, the manufacture of this cream became more complex, involving natural plant dyes and minerals extracted from fruits such as wild blackberries as fixatives for pigments.

Native American tribes made imaginative use of their natural surroundings for beauty accessories. Shells, beads, feathers, colored stones, and animal teeth were used as jewelry. Most Indians carried body paints with them in pouches at all times.

Each tribe had its individual preferences in the art of self-beautification. Elaborate tattooing was practiced by the Calusa of Florida. Among the Miwok of California certain natural head deformations, such as skulls with clearly defined flat places and long, angular foreheads, were considered highly attractive. In other tribes these head deformations were actively cultivated by binding infants' heads to cradle boards to flatten them. Women belonging to the Teton tribe of Dakota parted their hair in the middle and painted the dividing line with vermilion, a bright scarlet pigment. The Haida painted heraldic crests on their faces every day.

In addition to being a source of religious and aesthetic expression, body painting had a therapeutic effect on the Indians. In times of distress, widows would paint lines below the eyes which represented tears. The body painting of the Thompson Indians (of southwestern British Columbia) reflected the quest for their personal guardian spirit as they passed through different phases of life. Missionaries who sought to "cure" the Indians of these pagan practices failed to realize what anthropologists now know: these adornment practices were an essential part of the culture that gave American Indians their sense of personal dignity.

Aphrodite

"What life is there, what delight, without golden Aphrodite?"
—Mimnermus, c. 650 B.C.

Aphrodite is the divine figure in Greek mythology renowned for her captivating beauty, who oversees the romantic interests of mortals. Although as Aphrodite she is known as a Greek goddess, she has her roots in western Asiatic deities. As the incarnation of the maternal element, she is akin to goddesses such as Isis of ancient Egypt, Ishtar of Sumerian culture, and Astarte of the Phoenicians. The Romans renamed her Venus.

To all of these ancient cultures, the birth of this goddess represented a moment in history when the stabilization of the human species occurred. To increase the survival power of the species, humans began to reproduce year-round. This evolutionary development led to ritualized behavior around and reverential attitudes toward sexual intercourse—in other words, the beginning of romance. Humans began to couple out of love. Aphrodite is the personification of this phenomenon. When her exquisitely elegant presence was introduced into the cosmos, humans ceased to have periodic regressions to a bestial state. (That is not to say, however, that we stopped behaving like beasts.) With the splendor of her beauty, Aphrodite compels procreation inspired by love.

Because of the particular human sentiments she represents, i.e., love, passion, and an appreciation for beautiful things and people, Aphrodite/Venus has been the subject of much poetry and art over the centuries. According to ancient mythology, one of her chief accomplishments was the orchestration of a marriage between Eros and Psyche who then gave birth to Bliss. Eros is the male god of love and sensuality, while Psyche is the goddess of the mind and spirit. This myth defines true love: a stormy merger between the beauty and passion of both body and mind, accomplished against great odds. Those who struggle through it are ultimately rewarded with genuine happiness, at least in the creation of the next generation. In addition to being the goddess of love, in Greek myth Aphrodite is also attributed with the invention of perfume. Helen of Troy, according to legend the most beautiful woman in the world, was supposedly wearing Aphrodite's aromatic recipe when she attracted her kidnapper Paris, an event that "launched a thousand ships."

See also: ADONIS, HELEN OF TROY

Applying Cosmetics

See: COSMETICS

Apricot

The apricot, a small, yellowish-orange fruit related to the peach and the plum, is an abundant source of beauty aids. The mashed pulp, rich in vitamin A, is used as a facial masque to bring enriching minerals to the anemic complexion, revitalize tired muscles, and neutralize unevenly tanned skin. Apricot pulp is used as an ingredient in skin creams,

Apricot

lotions, shampoos, and conditioners because it returns moisture to the skin and scalp. The crushed pit of the apricot can be used in exfoliation (the process of removing dead skin cells from the skin's surface). Many commercial facial scrubs are made with ground apricot pits; their deep-cleansing properties prevent blackheads and sallow complexions. Used in massage, apricot oil has a psychically soothing effect.

How to Make an Apricot Mask

- Peel and pit two to three ripe apricots.
- Mash the pulp into a paste.
- Apply evenly to face and neck.
- Allow the mask to set, keeping facial muscles relaxed, for about forty-five minutes.
- Rinse with cool water and pat dry.

Aristotle

Aristotle, who lived from 384 to 322 B.C., was a highly influential philosopher during the Golden Age of Athens. He surveyed the entire spectrum of human knowledge available to the Mediterranean world during his day and his ideas form a significant part of the bedrock of Western civilization.

Although Aristotle's own writing style is far less poetic than that of many other philosophers', he had great reverence for beauty and the arts. For him, beauty was an essential element of human happiness.

Aristotle's philosophy rests on the axiom that happiness is the fundamental goal of human existence. He defined happiness as the activity of the soul in accordance with virtue, although in his list of virtues he includes such less-than-obvious qualities as magnificence (as a host, sensualist, and man of fashion), temperance, and liberality. This is because Aristotle concluded that, more than sound moral habits, one needs a degree of prosperity, joy in one's children, and good looks in order to achieve happiness. While it may sound self-evident, Aristotle was making a profound (and decidedly undemocratic) contribution to philosophic discourse when he wrote: "A man who is very ugly or lowborn or alone and childless is not apt to be very happy." For Aristotle's culture "childless" meant that one did not have any male children and "low-born" implied that one was not in a position to own slaves. Thus, by modern American standards this claim would be viewed as silly if not outright fallacious. However, like Aristotle and his fellow Athenians, Americans continue to believe in a correspondence between happiness and beauty. But if artistic representations are to be trusted, Aristotle did not exactly meet the classical criteria for physical beauty, yet by all accounts he led a long and happy life. Perhaps this should indicate that Aristotle desired that the virtue of "liberality" be applied to conceptions of beauty as well as ugliness.

Aromatherapy

Aromatherapy is the use of essential oils from plants and some animal extracts as a medicinal and beauty care treatment. An aromatherapist strives to match the unique essence in various plants with a person's unique body chemistry and needs. It is a holistic practice that presupposes a continuity between mind and body, health and beauty, pleasure and healing. The wisdom of aromatherapy begins in the nose. It is based on empirical demonstrations that natural fragrances have powerful chemical properties that can be tapped for physical and mental healing in addition to basic sensual pleasure.

The roots of aromatherapy date back to antiquity. Plant essences play a significant role in the medicinal and cosmetic lore of ancient Egypt, China, Greece, and India (where it is still religiously followed, even in hospitals). In addition, essential oils have been used in the manufacturing of perfume for centuries. Aromatherapy was transformed into a comprehensive cosmetic, physical, and mental science through the work of a French chemist named Gatfosse; an Austrian biochemist, Marguerite Maury; and a French physician and botanist, Dr. Jean Valnet.

Although aromatherapists utilize many different parts of plants (their leaves, flower petals, roots, and bark), aromatherapy is most noted for the use of essential oils derived from these various parts. Essential oils, or *essences,* are highly concentrated, aromatic substances usually extracted from plants through distillation. The procurement of essences requires careful timing and precision in each phase of the process: from the cultivation of the plants to harvest to chemical preparation. Even after the small, exquisite yield of oil has been acquired from a harvest of, say, thousands of rose petals, it requires careful storage due to its extreme volatility.

Because unadulterated essential oils are so concentrated, they are used in tiny doses. They work best when diluted. They may be diluted in bath water or in a humidifier, combined with other oils to treat the skin directly, or inhaled from a bottle. Aromatherapists apply essential oils in the form of creams, sprays, lotions, oral solutions, and massage oils. There are now several cosmetic lines that use plant essences and the principles of aromatherapy in the manufacture of shampoos, hair gels and sprays, conditioners, body oils, soaps, and facial masks.

Aromatherapy employs a wide range of plants for a variety of remedies. Doctors and cosmeticians, especially in France, have recorded astonishing successes using careful selected essential oils to cure an impressive array of health and beauty problems, ranging from mild physical blemishes to near-fatal illnesses. Some oils can stimulate drainage of the lymph glands which leads to the disintegration of cellulite. Other oils draw certain wastes directly out of the skin. Aromatherapy has also been used successfully to cure acne, retard aging, treat migraines and arthritis, improve mental well-being, and enhance powers of concentration. As this new-old science continues to intrigue the medical, cosmetological, and consumer communities, more research money, literature, and aromatically therapeutic products are becoming available.

See also: ESSENCE

List of Common Essential Oils and Their Uses

Cinnamon—energy

Cypress—broken veins

Geranium—dry skin

Jasmine—aphrodisiac

Juniper—improved circulation

Lavender—oily skin, aches, muscle pains, combating tension

Neroli—sensitive skin

Ylang-ylang—calming frazzled nerves

Art and Ideal Feminine Beauty

Since the aesthetics of a culture are intricately tied to a whole range of forces—religious, economic, political, and intellectual—the history of art reveals a great deal of information about the social history of human beings in general. At the very least, the painting and sculpture reflect certain aesthetic values, particularly with regard to the human body. This dynamic works both ways, however, since the ideals of beauty propagated in great works of art become an entrenched part of the cultural unconscious and actually dictate to some degree what humans in a given age see as desirable.

As styles and themes of art change, the one consistent point of departure for painters and sculptors is the nude human figure. (This is true even in periods when the human form was routinely concealed.) Historically, female models have been the preference of artists. Arguably, this is because the female body is largely composed of curves. Throughout the history of art, the curve, viewed compositionally as lyrical, gentle, warm, comforting, and "natural," has always been considered the most aesthetically pleasing line. For whatever reason, exploration of the female form has remained a fairly constant enterprise; however, the particular depiction of ideal femininity has varied tremendously.

Ancient Art. Egyptian carvings, statuary, and wall paintings demonstrate a preference for women with high cheekbones, large, almond-shaped eyes heightened with cosmetics, and lean, slight, firm, angular bodies. The ancient Greeks shared with the Egyptians a belief that the perfection of the human spirit should be reflected in the perfection of the human body, but they defined the perfect body differently. The Greeks emphasized proportion, balance, stature, and pronounced musculature. Their sculpture indicates a preference for handsome, manly women—not surprising, considering the marginal status of women in Greek society. The firm breasts and stomach, majestic height, and masculine features of the *Mourning Athena* and the *Venus de Milo* provide perfect examples of this ideal.

Middle Ages. In the art of the Middle Ages, also known as the Age of Faith, the body in general and the female body in particular were almost always hidden. When the body is revealed in medieval painting, as in Hieronymus Bosch's triptych *The Garden of Earthly Delights,* it takes on a sinister character meant to symbolize human depravity, sin, and damnation. Celebration of the physical form was dismissed as pagan; a Christian was encouraged to see the body as a mere shell, a prison for the soul until it was released to the true life that comes after death. Virtually all of the artwork created during the medieval period (roughly the fifth to the fifteenth centuries) employed sacred themes and was made for the greater glory of the Christian god. Because the body was perceived as a burdensome instrument of sin, it was kept safely concealed. (Even bathing was considered an unholy and even obscene practice because it involved such extreme exposure.) In the paintings of this period, women's bodies were buried under long robes that hung in straight, flat lines. At the end of the fifteenth century, the naked female body returned to European art in paintings whose themes were sorcery and witchcraft, such as *The Charm of Love* by the Master of Niederheim. In this painting, the blond sorceress is mixing a love potion with nothing on but her wild, loose hair and sandals made of thorns!

Renaissance. The transition from medieval to Renaissance art is marked by the work of Dürer. His early sketches of the female form are tentative and portray realistic, touchingly imperfect bodies. His later work shows both increased confidence and the sacrifice of naturalism in order to hint at an ideal—the plump peasant girls he sketched were transformed into slimmer, smoother skinned Eves.

With the birth of humanism during the Italian Renaissance through the rediscovery of classical learning, the acceptable themes and representations of the human figure expanded a great deal. The status of women—and their bodies—improved considerably. Botticelli's *The Birth of Venus* (c. 1485) reflects an admiration for the gentle curves of the female form, perfect proportions, and alabaster skin. Even more important, the appealing manner in which this Venus lounges in her nudity suggests an appreciation for female sensuality that had been absent in an era prone to burning the most vaguely promiscuous or eccentric women as witches. Botticelli's Venus is so beautiful that it is difficult to detect the unnatural length of her neck and torso and the steep drop of her shoulders; these liberties are taken in the interest of creating a more graceful line and emphasizing both the tenderness and majesty of the goddess of love. Raphael, the youngest member of the High Renaissance triumvirate which also included Michelangelo and Leonardo, showed his reverence for the female form in his painting of *The Three Graces* (1504–5), which depicts the same body from three different angles. This was painted at a time when it was still unlawful to draw from living naked models. However, the rendering is quite convincing, if slightly ethereal. By the time Giorgione painted *Concert Champetre*, an arcadian landscape with musicians including two robust nude women as symbols of beauty, the Greek ideal of the beautiful body (that which is most masculine) had been completely reversed. The female shape itself had become synonymous with beauty.

One of the most important contributions made during this time to the art of representing human beings was the responsibility of Leonardo da Vinci. Acutely interested in anatomical study, he wanted to capture the sense of motion characteristic of living creatures. He believed that images of the human body rendered in paint tended to look hard, frozen in time. As a matter of fact, for the Italian quattrocento masters and the likes of Van Eyck, beauty was synonymous with stillness; therefore, their human figures tend to look more like statues than breathing flesh and blood. In creating one of his most sublime masterpieces, the portrait of the Florentine lady known as the *Mona Lisa* (c. 1502), Leonardo found the solution. His revolutionary technique is called "sfumato" and it entails the blurring of outlines and softening of colors to allow for ambiguity—shapes go in and out of focus, creating the effect of motion within the picture. Leonardo applied this technique to the corners of Lisa's mouth and eyes and around her hands, the most expressive regions of the human body. The vitality of Mona Lisa's face, the ghostly quality of her smile, the intelligence behind her eyes, and her massive presence which seems to eclipse the landscape behind her, all suggest a new respect for the complexity and depth of feminine beauty.

One of the first blatantly erotic renderings of the female body in Western art is by Tintoretto. His *Susannah and the Elders* (c. 1550) depicts a woman wallowing in the exuberance of her substantial flesh as we, along with the elders, look on. This fascination with the voluptuous woman increases with the passage of time. Or perhaps it is more accurate to state that the "ideal" becomes more "real" as time goes by. In the seventeenth and eighteenth century in Europe (as remains true to this day in many traditional societies), fat was a symbol of opulence and, therefore, considered beautiful.

Baroque. During the Baroque era (approximately 1600 to 1750), the dominant portrayer of the female form was the great Flemish painter Rubens. Rubens had a preference (in life as well as art) for women with cherubic, carefree plumpness. In such paintings as *Rape of the Daughters of Leucippus* (1618), he seems to relish the cellulite of well-nourished women. The two women who seem to resist their abductors rather reluctantly are not burdened but empowered by their tremendous thighs, bottoms, and breasts. In fact, this is what makes them irresistible to the gods who are trying to carry them off.

In spite of his obvious appreciation for the exceedingly full-figured woman, Rubens, like other painters of this era, has been accused of reducing women to objects of male desire. This is something Rembrandt, the greatest figure of the late Baroque period, did not do. His paintings capture the vulnerability of the female body, demanding somehow that his viewers love, not lust after, his female figures. Also, the neo-classical painters such as Ingres and David seem to have revered the power of the female body; their nudes eye the viewer candidly, secure in their smooth curves and perfect porcelain skin. However, Ingres's women are so obviously idealized that they are perceived more as goddesses than as mere mortals.

Late Eighteenth and Nineteenth Centuries. Late eighteenth century paintings, particularly those produced in England, depict the female form tightly corseted and rigid, as if to suggest that the most beautiful female body is one that is kept under lock and key.

The nineteenth century, with its Victorian ethic and prudish, prurient society, witnessed a decline in respect for sensuality and women in general. Ironically, however, the painters of the period far from shunned the nude study. French academy painting, with its token classical references, seems hardly more than an excuse for eroticism at the expense of women. But this reduction of the feminine in art was eventually transcended by the Impressionist movement. The Impressionists strove for a new kind of honesty in studies of the female nude in which character became a more significant aspect of beauty than some idealized form. Meanwhile, the new medium of photography was being used to create romanticized images of women.

Twentieth Century. During the first decade of the twentieth century with the Cubist revolution, the female form seemed to lose its place of prominence as it was abstracted and fragmented by Picasso and Braque. But as a subject, it quickly returned, although not as a focus or symbol of beauty per se. As a matter of fact, the very notion of beauty itself became an object of scorn among the fine arts intelligentsia. This reflected (and continues to reflect) the desire to demystify art, shatter notions of absolute truth, and spare women the indignity of objectification. Renderings of the female body have become increasingly psychological and private, expressing the sense of alienation and distrust of traditional values characteristic of this century.

But obviously the process of celebrating, exploiting, and prescribing guidelines for the aesthetically pleasing female form has not exactly disappeared from our culture. These preoccupations have simply receded from the realm of art and taken up a dominant place in other visual media such as film and, especially, advertising. The effect has been both the diversification and the inordinate elevation of the criteria of female beauty. On one hand, as the world becomes "smaller," advertisements build an awareness of other cultures and ideals through the inclusion of nontraditional, exotic conceptions of beauty. On the other hand, computer technology, which allows for the radical manipulation of images, has made possible the production of ridiculously high standards of ideal feminine beauty: long-limbed, lean, muscular, full-breasted, perfectly tanned, flawlessly symmetrical female bodies. In light of reality—that human beauty is inevitably subject to and even depends on irregularities—these images are likely to confuse and oppress both women and men.

As is apparent from the previous examples, the obsession with the human body and its representation has been, and will continue to be, a crucial expression in the struggle to understand the meaning of human existence.

Astringent

An astringent is any substance which contracts or "tightens" skin tissue. Tonics, toners, clarifying lotions, fresheners, and exfoliating lotions are all astringents. Although many substances have astringent properties, the one used most often in cosmetics is alcohol.

Especially useful on oily skin, an astringent should be used after the skin has been cleaned with an alkaline product such as soap or cleansing cream. Wipe any alcohol-based astringent across the skin with a cotton ball. It will eliminate any soapy residue and dead skin cells, deeply clean dirt from the skin's pores, and restore the acid balance of the skin. It also produces a refreshing, invigorating sensation.

Excessive use of astringents may irritate the skin. They should not be used on dry skin, as they will further exacerbate the dry condition.

See also: ALCOHOL, pH BALANCE, TANNIC ACID

Baldness

Alopecia, or baldness, is derived from the Greek word for fox— *alopex*—because foxes commonly had mange, which resulted in hair loss. When hair follicles die and can no longer produce fresh hair growth, baldness occurs.

What causes baldness? The Hagerians, native peoples of New Guinea, believe baldness is a sign that the protective ghosts have deserted a person. As recently as the nineteenth century, Westerners believed that hair loss was the result of overfrequent hair cuts and wearing tight hats. Baldness in some cultures is also associated with control (or loss) of passion. Hippocrates, the father of medicine, proposed a somewhat contradictory hypothesis claiming a directly proportional relationship between baldness and virility (possibly because he himself was bald!).

Hippocrates's reasoning was that the excessive hot-bloodedness of some men causes their hair to get overheated at the roots and fall out. The myth that bald men are more amorous has lasted up to the present day, perhaps proving the power of a self-serving prophesy to be self-fulfilling!

Scientists have now demonstrated that baldness is genetically determined, and that genes for baldness are carried on nonsex-linked chromosomes. However, in order for baldness to manifest itself, androgens, the hormones that induce male sexual development, must be present, which is why baldness is primarily a masculine fate. Baldness is also more marked in men because men are initially endowed with fewer hair follicles per square inch of scalp than women. Thus, hair loss is more easily discernible in males. By the age of fifty, 60 percent of all white males experience some degree of hair loss, and many begin showing signs of hair loss as early as the age of twenty. Baldness is much less frequent among Orientals and Blacks.

The likelihood of baldness in men or women can be increased. Stress, which causes a tightening of the scalp, increases the odds of hair loss. Baldness can also be caused or accelerated by scalp infections, radiation, excess heat, environmental pollutants, and by a reaction to drugs, such as amphetamines, thyroid medications, anticancer drugs, and any preparations with sex hormones. Short-term hair loss or thinning of the hair can occur during pregnancy and illness.

Products containing an antibaldness compound derived from retinol (related to a substance currently used in some acne medications), are expected to enter the United States market soon. Some products come close to curing baldness, claiming to arrest hair loss. None is universally approved by the medical community yet. The only definite cure for baldness available at the present time is castration! However, for many men, hair transplants or toupees are a satisfactory alternative to baldness. Scalp reduction surgery (a surgical procedure involving the removal and tightening of skin near the forehead or the base of the neck) and scalp-flap surgery to curb receding hairlines are more dramatic (as well as more expensive and risky) means for intervention. Maybe the most effective strategy for countering baldness would be to dethrone the Samson myth, which locates the source of male virility in the hair as opposed to in the attitude of a man.

See also: HAIR TRANSPLANTS, HAIR WEAVING, TOUPEE

Barbershop

In ancient Rome and Athens, the barbershop was the center for gossip among the fashionable men of the elite. It has always been a place for

Barber pole from the late nineteenth century

the exchange of information—particularly, about the latest fashions—as well as for the doctoring of physical appearance. The barbershop remained a center for social stimulus in the 1500s when musical entertainment was provided while men received a shave or trim. Today, barbershops are less frequently patronized than unisex hair salons, although a remnant of the barbershop phenomenon is still discernible in small towns in the United States.

The emblem of the barbershop—the red-and-white striped pole—is left over from the Middle Ages, when barbers and surgeons were one and the same. The stripes on the barber's pole represented the bandage with which he wrapped his patient following the bloodletting procedure commonly performed then in hopes of ridding the body of impurities.

See also: BEAUTY PARLORS

Bathing

"I have had a good many more uplifting thoughts, creative and expansive visions—while soaking in comfortable baths or drying myself after bracing showers—in well-equipped American bathrooms than I have ever had in any cathedral."
—Edmund Wilson, *A Piece of My Mind*

In most civilizations, bathing has been perceived as a relaxing, restorative activity as well as a means of getting clean. The parallel between the bath and the mythic fountain of youth is not purely metaphoric. Regular and conscientious bathing is both physically and mentally therapeutic. The ancient Romans revered the bath so highly that it was a special social ritual. The same is true of the Japanese today.

When interaction between the East and West was established during and after the Crusades in the twelfth and thirteenth centuries, ancient Eastern tribes and civilizations were horrified by the lack of hygiene they saw among Westerners. It was not until the nineteenth century that Western Europeans came to understand the benefits of regular bathing. At this time, "Cleanliness is next to godliness" was taken up as a manifesto. The phrase is extracted from a sermon given by John Wesley in the late eighteenth century, but it is actually a paraphrase from a more ancient Eastern text.

While the Romans nearly perfected the technology for baths with their impressive terra-cotta aqueducts, many cultures have contributed formulas for healthy and sensual bathwater. Sixteenth century poet Ben Jonson recommended "the juice of July flowers, spirit of roses and violets, the milk of unicorns and panther's breath, gathered in bags and mixed with wines." If a person isn't fortunate enough to have those

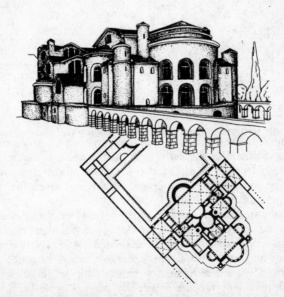

Roman baths in Trier, Germany. For Romans, bathing was an important social event.

items on hand, many other options are readily available. In concocting new bathing products, manufacturers combine modern technology with old wisdom about sensory pleasures.

Many would agree with Voltaire, the eighteenth century French philosopher, who claimed that the perfumed bath is "the luxury of luxuries." Many elaborate recipes have been developed over the centuries, and some of the most delicate bath crystals manufactured today are derived from natural ingredients such as dried flowers, herbs, pine needles, crushed grains (such as oatmeal), strawberries, and raspberries. Lemon juice added to a bath cools the temperature of the skin and, like oatmeal, neutralizes the skin's moisture, meaning it either eliminates excess oil or moisturizes the skin as needed. Despite their mythic reputations for softening the skin, milk and honey are better left in the kitchen. In their pure form, their messiness far outweighs their value. Their benefits are best attained in the form of modern cosmetic products. Manufacturers extract their essential properties in the laboratory.

Below is a list of flowers and herbs which accomplish specific restorative tasks when used in the bath:

Improving Skin	Easing Aches	Calming
ginseng	bay leaves	peppermint
comfrey	nutmeg	chamomile
lemon verbena	oregano	valerian root
cloves	hay flower	thyme
goldenrod	wintergreen	passionflower
Saint-John's-wort	iris	hops
red raspberry	deadly nightshade	tiger lily

The herbs listed above may be purchased in most health food stores in bulk. To use them in the bath, tie a small portion in several layers of cheesecloth. Herbal teas are another source for procuring many of these herbs. Also look for bath oils, crystals, and jellies which list these particular herbs as ingredients.

Bath salts are designed to soften and perfume water. Some less expensive bath oils and foaming salts that are made to produce lather actually dry the skin. This is due to the presence of sulfonated oils among their contents.

Because human body fluids are similar to seawater, bathing in sea salts or Epsom salts is a healthy moisturizing technique because saline solutions are readily absorbed through the pores. During World War II, medics in the U. S. army discovered that a bath of seawater and baking soda helps the human body rid itself of the pollutants and radiation that abound in the environment. (Sea salts soften water by exchanging sodium ions for those of calcium and magnesium, which counters the adverse charge generated by exposure to radiation.) Radiation from the atomic bombs dropped on Japan affected a multitude of people in subtle as well as gruesome ways. This kind of bath was helpful in treating the minor skin and nervous disorders of the Japanese people. Today one would be hard-pressed to find a spot on the planet utterly free from radiation and poisonous chemicals.

How to Prepare a Healthful Sea Salt Bath

A weekly sea salt bath is healthful for anyone except sufferers from heart conditions or high blood pressure. It purges the body of poisonous wastes, dissolves urates, and neutralizes toxins in the blood stream and tissues, and softens the skin. Sea salt can be purchased at any natural foods store. Here are the steps to follow:

- Put 1 inch of hot water (120°F) in a tub.
- Add one pound of salts; mix well.
- Sit in the tub while slowly adding another inch of water.
- Rub body with a soft towel dipped in the salt water.
- Add another inch of water and another pound of salt.
- Slowly add another inch of water and another pound.
- Rub the body gently from head to feet with the towel.
- Stop when sweat breaks out on your forehead; the treatment is complete.
- Follow with a brief, cool shower.

Beards

The men of the Mesopotamian civilization curled their beards into numerous, tight, shell-like whorls interwoven with gold thread. Ancient Egyptians grew beards as a sign of mourning; otherwise, beards were reserved for rulers. Even female rulers wore artificial beards as a symbol of authority. In ancient Greece, a beard marked the philosopher and was a symbol of his freedom from worldly concerns.

Beards are largely perceived as a symbol of masculine virility, especially in pagan traditions. This is why in the medieval Christian church men were commanded to shave their beards on the day before Good Friday so that they would be "honest" (or chaste) for Easter. Women who were unfortunate enough to grow beards (the result of hormonal imbalances) were dubbed witches.

In 1710, Czar Peter the Great of Russia outlawed beards but first imposed a tax on them before they could be shaved off as a means of generating some quick revenue!

In the twentieth century, the majority of men are clean shaven or wear only a mustache. However, the beard did experience a brief resurgence of popularity during the late 1960s and 1970s in the United States.

Aside from personal preference, beards are a worthy option for covering scars or bad skin conditions. Mustaches minimize protruding lips, add dimension to flat profiles, and soften prominent noses. The general aesthetic rule for beard grooming is that the hair and beard be coordinated, creating relative symmetry between skull and chin. For example, a full beard works best with a full head of hair, and a closely cropped beard complements a shorter or more sculpted hairstyle.

How to Maintain a Well-Groomed Beard

- Keep the beard as clean and well combed as you do your hair.
- Trim the entire beard every two weeks or as needed. Give special attention to the mustache, which should be clipped from the bottom up. (Note: Closely cropped beards are considered more appropriate for the business world; fuller beards are associated with academics and scientists.)
- The mustache should blend into the beard. Unruly hairs can be trained with mustache wax, which is made to resist food stains, dirt, and dust and is generally weatherproof.

"Beauty and the Beast"

Beauty is a recurring theme in all sorts of literature, including fairy tales. Like beauty, stories are an intrinsic part of human culture. Fairy tales provide a powerful and subtle means for a culture to transmit its values and ideals. Folk and fairy tales were originally passed down orally from generation to generation. Most renditions as we know them today are the result of a scholarly endeavor by two Germans, Jacob and Wilhelm Grimm. They traveled throughout the countryside collecting these stories which were originally published for adults. The simple, yet vividly descriptive style of fairy tales accounts for their popular appeal.

A large number of these tales, for example, "Cinderella," "Snow White," and "The Frog Prince," as well as "Beauty and the Beast," focus on the relationship between spiritual and physical transformation, or inner and outer beauty. "Beauty and the Beast" has more variations than any other story and recurs throughout many different cultures. The theme itself is ancient.

In the story of "Beauty and the Beast," the ordinary and the fantastic coexist. The heroine is a beautiful young girl named Beauty whose physical beauty, like Cinderella's, reflects the spiritual beauty which permeates her inner being.

Beauty is adored by her father and envied by her sisters. The father is suddenly stripped of his wealth. He embarks on a journey to try to regain his lost riches, but his attempts prove unsuccessful. On his way home, he steals some roses to bring home to Beauty, his youngest daughter, as a gift. He is caught in the act by a terrifying beast who demands his life in retribution. In most versions of this tale, the form of the Beast is left to the imagination although in some cases the Beast takes the shape of a snake. After hearing the man describe his lovely daughter and seeing the depth of his love for her, the Beast softens and releases him. He bestows upon him a chest of gold, after eliciting the father's promise to return in three months time to die. The father returns home and tells the story of his trip to Beauty, who not only defends him against the wrath of her selfish sisters, but also offers to die in his place. When the time comes, the Beast spares her life by convincing her to remain with him in his castle. There, all of her wishes are satisfied, but she is terribly lonely. Eventually, she grows to look forward to the Beast's nightly visits at dinner, which she initially dreaded. Every night he patiently asks for her hand in marriage, and every night she politely refuses. A brief separation and the near death of the Beast proves that a mutual need and affection has developed between them. In the end, she agrees to marry him. At the moment Beauty agrees to the marriage, the Beast is transformed into a handsome prince. The father rejoins them and takes up a new role in Beauty's life, one that is respectable if not primary. They all live happily ever after.

"Beauty and the Beast" provides a lesson in the nature of beauty and the transforming and redeeming power of love. As the story progresses,

Beauty learns new ways of seeing, with her heart and mind instead of just her eyes. Only then can she recognize the beauty within the monster. Through this act of love, the Beast is transformed. However, this process is not the result of pure magic; it develops through interaction and over time. There are many insights to be gleaned here: genuine love grows gradually, initial skepticism may be an essential part of solidifying romantic love, and that a gift acquired painlessly without sacrifice lacks ultimate value and is often as quickly abandoned as it was attained.

The love between Beauty and her Beast is born of a slowly developed friendship. It creates new beauty through the union of mind/spirit (Beauty) with body (the Beast). On another level, the symbols work inversely as well—Beauty has physical beauty while the beast has inner beauty. He is both generous and gentle with her throughout. This union between the two aspects of humanity is essential for genuine love between people, but it must also take place within an individual in order for one to attain a balanced sense of self.

This story figuratively represents a process that allows romantic love to evolve in time, thereby eventually bringing happiness to parent, matured child, and spouse alike. The father makes way for the next generation; the adoring girl becomes a strong, nurturing woman; and the Beast becomes a lovable as well as loving man. All of the central figures encounter tremendous trials. In coping with these hardships—the Beast's physical deformity, the father's loss of his livelihood, and Beauty's sacrifice to spare her father's life—each gains strength and, ultimately, a deep understanding of the beautiful. The story traces their personal journey toward communal, not solitary sublimity. It is a quest that equates beauty with progress, genuine love, and the perpetuation of life.

Beauty Marks

A beauty mark is actually a common genetic abnormality, known as a mole or nevus, located on the face. In eighteenth century France it was not uncommon for women of fashion to create beauty marks artificially with tiny black patches of cloth. Not only were these spots thought to emphasize the beauty or whiteness of the skin, they were also used as a fairly elaborate message system. For example, a specific shape or location of the beauty mark denoted a political affiliation. When Marilyn Monroe was reigning sex goddess of the silver screen during the fifties, many women began once again to accentuate their own or create artificial beauty marks in mimicry of the prominent black nevus she emphasized with black eyeliner just above the left corner of her sultry lips.

Beauty Pageants

In the twentieth century, the emphasis on beauty has been increasingly associated with a healthy, well-formed body. These values became ritualized in America in 1921 with the institution of Atlantic City's Miss America pageant, now the most famous and longest running beauty competition in the world. At the first Miss America pageant, a two-day carnival held on September 7 and 8 at Keith's Theatre on Garden Pier, sixteen-year-old Margaret Gorman of Washington, D.C. was declared the winner. Her measurements were 30-25-32 and, at five feet one inch, she weighed 108 pounds—tiny by today's standards. Those early pageants were held right on the beach and all participants, including the judges and the policemen who provided security at the event wore bathing attire.

Beauty and how it is represented often has political repercussions. The Miss America pageant, for example, has a long history of inciting emotional attacks from dramatically different camps, from religious fundamentalists to feminist crusaders. The latter, in the form of the modern women's liberation movement, were given their first genuine visibility as a result of protests conducted on the Boardwalk during the 1969 pageant. The fundamentalists object to what is perceived as sexual exploitation on moralistic grounds.

The connection between social ritual and beauty is apparent in examining a beauty pageant. Rituals trigger emotionally charged responses. Because rituals celebrate the primal needs and beliefs of a community, it is only natural that people react passionately against rites they feel contradict or undermine the values to which they are committed. The Miss America pageant satisfies many of the prescriptions of human ritual. It involves spectacle and elements of magic, and it glorifies a basic biological impulse—that of personal beautification. Symbolically, this ritual can be understood as a demonstration of how a behavior which we share with other creatures in the natural world is elaborated in a uniquely human fashion—the longing for transcendence. By crowning a goddess, we playfully obscure the lines between mortal and divine for a few hours.

In the early days of this pageant, the ritualistic aspects of the ceremony were more pronounced. Contestants dressed in exotic costumes and struck bizarre, provocative poses for the judges. Extravaganza remains the defining characteristic of the competition. When the pageant moved indoors into the Convention Hall in 1940, observers described the scene as a "veritable fairyland." When the show entered the television era starting in 1954, the indulgence in spectacle increased greatly.

Miss America is consistently one of the highest rated television programs of the year internationally. It has averaged a viewing audience of twenty-five to twenty-eight million homes per year since 1958.

Through a statistical compilation the following composite portrait of Miss America can be determined: She is 19.35 years old, five feet six inches tall weighing 119 pounds, with brown hair, blue eyes, fair complexion, and measurements of 34.9-23.9-35.4.

But over time, Miss America has moved away from the prototype. Bess Myerson, Miss America of 1945, was a serious musician who was awarded the first academic scholarship. She was also the first Jewish Miss America and the only person from New York City ever to attain the title. She went on to become an active politician. The first black contestant in the Miss America Pageant was Cheryl Adrienne Browne of Jamaica, New York. She was a sophomore at Luther College in Iowa when she was selected to represent that state in the 1970 competition.

Over time, the pageant has expanded its definition of beauty to include and even emphasize achievements in the realms of academia, the arts, and civics. Today, Miss America pageants (local and national combined) are the number-one source of college scholarship money for women. In recent years, the pageant has moved increasingly away from the stereotypical American beauty in its selection of winners.

The Miss America Pageant is the most extravagant, but it is actually only one among hundreds of beauty competitions sponsored annually all around the world. Most American towns hold their own beauty contests. Among these include such whimsical events as the Apple Blossom Queen (Wenatchee, Washington), Miss New York Subways Contest, New Jersey Seafood Princess (Pt. Pleasant), and the Queen of Love and Beauty (St. Louis, Missouri). Every year in Sturgis, South Dakota, there is a beauty competition between motorcycles (not their owners) at the annual Harley-Davidson rally! In West Africa, the Fulani have a beauty contest for young boys. They display their elaborately decorated bodies in front of the young, unmarried girls. As one part of the competition, the boys submit to whipping as a test of endurance.

See also: BODY

Beauty Parlors

Beauty parlors traditionally were either: elegant and exotic, elaborately decorated with expensive furnishings, dim lighting, and heavily scented; or hygienic and scientific, sterile, and brightly lit. They proliferated in the nineteen twenties with the craze for bobbed hair. Now beauty parlors are more commonly known as beauty salons and are widely divergent in design and format. They usually cultivate the patronage of both sexes.

See also: BARBERSHOP

Beauty Plants

Plants play a central role in beauty culture in numerous ways. Human beings have always sought to order natural beauty so that human civilization itself is enriched and even transformed. We cultivate and nurture plants not only for food but also for the enhancement of the interior and exterior of our homes, workplaces, public spaces, and individual bodies.

Historically, plants have been the primary source of cosmetics (as well as of medicines). After many years in which the cosmetic industry has been dominated by synthetic manufacturing, natural cosmetics are coming back into vogue. Hair and bath products, perfumes, makeup, and even dentifrices made largely from unadulterated plant substances have become a viable, more healthful alternative to synthetic products. Several biotically based cosmetic lines are distributed through beauty salons or sold in natural food stores nationwide.

Beautiful plants are a part of all important human rituals. Churches are typically decorated with fresh flowers every week; we send flowers for birthdays, anniversaries, funerals, and showers; we adorn ourselves with flower wreaths or corsages or weave flowers into our hair for high holidays and celebrations. Plants and cut flowers are always a welcome gift—no matter what the occasion.

Although it is arguable that all plants are beautiful, some plants have names that emphasize their connection with human aesthetics. Here are a few examples.

American beauty berry is a hearty, vigorous shrub native to the Eastern seaboard, the South, and the Southwest. It is notable for its showy purple berries that attract birds. People have used the berries to make paints.

American Beauty rose is a classic hybrid tea famous for its exuberant shrubbery and for the intense red color and delicate perfume of its flowers. In general, the rose is a symbol of beauty in many cultures, but this rose is one of the honored few which has the word "beauty" included in its name.

Beauty bush is an ornamental flowering shrub native to central China. It is a member of the honeysuckle family and the only member of its genus. In early summer, its bell-shaped, pink flowers bloom in pairs, grouped one above the other. The blossoms are superseded by bristly fruit which remain until the thick of winter. This plant earns its name because it is both visually stunning and hardy.

"*Beauty leaf*" is the name given to the Alexandrian laurel or Dilo oil tree. It is chiefly an ornamental plant, native to tropical Asia. It is cultivated for its glossy, leathery foliage and fragrant, petite, white flowers. These flowers grow in sprays from pale yellow stalks. These trees are often used in landscaping near the ocean because they are resistant to sea spray. They reach a height of sixteen to nineteen meters, or fifty to sixty feet. Dilo, a medicinal oil, is extracted from the seeds. Like a beautiful person, this plant is healing as "a sight for sore eyes" as well as literally providing a medicinal property from its core.

See also: AROMATHERAPY, NATURAL COSMETICS, ROSES

Beer

The notion that stale beer used as a rinse enhances the hair's body is now fortified by solid evidence. Beer is an effective conditioner because its primary ingredients—malted barley and hops—are protein rich.

Wild barley

How to Use a Beer Rinse

- Open a can or bottle of beer and leave it open at room temperature overnight.
- When showering the next day, wash the hair, preferably with a biodegradable shampoo. Rinse hair thoroughly.
- Pour the beer through clean hair and leave it for several minutes while massaging the scalp and longer strands of hair.
- Rinse completely.

Bernhardt, Sarah

Sarah Bernhardt (1844–1923) was a French-born actress and beauty famous for creation of roles in the "grand style." The French artist Mucha painted her portrait on numerous occasions. However, she did not correspond to the culturally accepted beauty ideals of her day. She was rapier thin, exceptionally tall for a woman, with very pale skin, a cloud of hair, a narrow nose and mouth, and luminous, bewitching eyes.

Her personal understanding of beauty was deeply entwined with the outrageous. She owned a pet tiger and, during her farewell tours, traveled about with a custom-measured, satin-lined coffin. She enjoyed shocking the masses by applying lipstick in public, and she would coat her hands with butter to keep them soft. Her charismatic personality and ice-breaking antics were instrumental in making public display of cosmetic adornment socially acceptable once again.

She delighted audiences on several continents during the late nineteenth and early twentieth century. She made quite a career out of a whole series of "farewell tours" in the United States! By then, she was noted equally well for her off-stage theatrics as those performed on stage. She played such historically famous beauties as Cleopatra and Camille.

Blush

> "Man is the only animal that blushes. .
> Or needs to."
> —Mark Twain, from
> *Pudd'nhead Wilson's
> New Calendar*

One of the most important features of an attractive fair-skinned face is a blushing cheek. It is a mark of health, vibrancy, youth, and, of course, embarrassment. When applied cosmetically, the intensity of any shade of blush attracts the eye. When used skillfully, blush highlights and subtly sculpts the contours of the face; when heavily or carelessly applied, it may appear clownish or tawdry.

During the nineteen fifties and nineteen sixties a dramatic, hollow-looking face was considered desirable. Today, a more natural-looking face is considered most appealing. This is why it is important to apply color with a brush in a line that sweeps above the cheekbone and fades as it approaches the temple. The zygomatic bones, or cheekbones, are the high swell of the cheek, located just below the eyes. After applying blush, blend the color so that no obvious line is visible. Powdered blushes are the most commonly employed since liquids require greater skill and are harder to control. Creams and gels are more economical since only a very small amount is needed.

Placing blush high on the cheekbones accentuates their prominence, while shading the area across the bones softens them. Vertical lines give the illusion of a thinner face; horizontal ones widen it. The choice should be determined by the shape of the individual face, but in general, a slightly diagonal, upward sweeping application is best.

Body

> *"There's language in her eye, her cheek, her lip,*
> *Nay, her foot speaks; her wanton spirits look out*
> *At every joint and motive of her body."*
> —Shakespeare, *Troilus and Cressida*

Knowledge about the human body is no longer the sole property of medical professionals, and, therefore, ignorance is no longer the pre-determined fate of the layperson. Fortified with basic information about human anatomy and physiology, every person can maximize the beauty and efficiency of his or her physique.

All of the complex features of the human body are formed from the division of a single fertilized cell. This single cell divides in a process called mitosis and, ultimately, about a hundred trillion cells—which together organize into tissues and organs—form the body. During life, about two hundred million cells are created every minute. Many replace themselves, a notable exception being brain cells. The lifespan of different types of cells varies greatly; some nerve and muscle cells are so resilient they can last a full lifetime.

Muscles account for one half of the healthy individual's weight. The body has over 650 muscles. Voluntary or skeletal muscles, such as those in the arms and legs, are consciously controlled by the cerebrospinal nervous system. Involuntary or smooth muscles found in internal organs listen to the sympathetic nervous system. Cardiac muscles control the action of the heart. Muscles can be stimulated by nerve impulses, massage, electric current, acids and salts, and infrared and ultraviolet rays.

The stimulation of muscles and nerves assists the functioning of glands and speeds the removal of toxins from the bloodstream. Body toxins are released equally in three different ways—through perspiration, the excretory channels, and breathing. The efficient operation of these processes lowers anxiety and improves physical well-being.

Muscles weigh more than fat. If two people are proportioned the same, the person who has the greatest percentage of muscle will actually weigh more. Numbers alone can be deceptive. Even though it increases body weight, conscious muscle development is essential to maintaining a healthy body. Exercise that develops the muscles of the body generally increases circulation as well. Good blood circulation is crucial to maintaining healthy hair, skin, and nails.

The composition of the body changes entirely every seven years. The fuel which runs this complicated, efficient machine is created from oxygen and from the nutrients and vitamins found in food. This is why knowledge about nutrition—when heeded and applied— can make a wealth of difference in an individual's general health, appearance, temperament, longevity, and energy level. Learning about nutrition takes a conscious effort, but the benefits of healthful eating can last a lifetime, while the success of fad diets tends to be marginal and short-lived.

America suffers from malnutrition due to overnutrition. The average American body is composed of 40 to 50 percent fat although 25 to 30 percent is the healthy ideal. Another problem is constipation from an excessively starchy and sugar-laden diet. It is a false assumption that age inevitably leads to a thickened middle. It is the result of years of slumping, overeating, and lack of exercise.

Even in this age that extols the virtues of physical fitness, most Americans lead a largely sedentary life and miss many opportunities to exercise while going through regular routines. Even without a disciplined exercise routine, many individuals could benefit by a few minor adjustments—for example, taking the stairs instead of the elevator when the trip is only a few flights up or down, or reaching and stretching consciously when retrieving objects which have fallen or are slightly out of range.

Different historical eras have celebrated a wide range of physical body types. Although these ideals have changed comparatively quickly in the West, a body in good physical condition, whatever the dimensions of the frame, now earns admiration.

Bodybuilding

Over fifty million people around the world have become obsessed with progressive-resistance exercise (contracting the muscles against resistance). Bodybuilding, also known as "pumping iron" or weight training, is the process of firming, shaping, heightening, and even rearranging the musculature of the body through the use of free weights or machines. Through weight training, it is possible to work individual muscles or sets of muscles directly for maximum stimulation and efficiency. Weight training also improves cardiovascular strength and flexibility.

Bodybuilding is becoming ever more popular among women because it is the fastest known way to transform the female figure. A conscientious, carefully designed program of weight training can produce visible results within three to five weeks. Reflecting the rise of this exercise-obsession, there are vast numbers of periodicals and other publications available that offer advice to the amateur and the competitor. Because this is the most strenuous pastime around, it is important to be well informed about the demands bodybuilding places on the body and follow several crucial prescriptions. If you have a severe weight problem or have little experience with fitness training, you should seek professional advice about how to increase your general activity level before trying to pump iron.

How to Begin Training with Weights

- Always warm up before beginning a routine.
- As a beginner, start slowly and perform short series.
- Commit to a nutritious diet centered on fresh, unprocessed foods.
- If intending to pursue weight training in earnest, see a doctor for a medical exam which includes a stress test and ask for dietary recommendations.
- Maintain concentration throughout workouts.
- Get seven to eight hours sleep every night.
- Practice self-scrutiny and consciously set reasonable, short-term goals.

Body Painting

Applying color to the body is a practice that dates back at least as far as Neanderthal man. People in cultures in every historical epoch and in every area of the globe have felt compelled to paint themselves.

The act of painting the body can be seen as an attempt by humans to communicate graphically what exists inside—both physically and emotionally. In traditional as well as in developed cultures, body paint is used to announce crises or turning points and to display membership in a communal order of values. It is also a means to celebrate the body itself and the joys and pains that go along with having one. For example, among the Sharanahua of Peru, a woman's beauty is judged completely by the skill with which her body paint is applied. This body paint is considered a crucial and natural part of seduction.

Body painting plays an especially important part in the lives of the Aborigines, the native peoples of Australia. Families spend many of their leisure hours improving each other's appearance with body paint. Using a wide-ranging palette of colors extracted from the natural world, they create original and personal designs and entertain each other with songs of heroic legends during the procedure. These personal designs are notably different from the highly symbolic, formulaic imagery Aborigines create in preparation for traditional rituals, such as the ceremony that announces coming of age. The traditional images are less playful than the personal designs and are usually images such as the emblems of their totemic ancestors. When they develop designs in their leisure hours, the purpose is solely to give the imagination free reign, not to reinforce tradition per se. The body paint of mourning among the Aborigines is notable for its conscious messiness. It expresses a belief that beauty and vanity are inappropriate for the bereaved. Therefore, the body is streaked randomly with a murky whitewash.

The color triad of red, black, and white appears cross-culturally in body painting and art. Anthropologist Dr. Victor Turner believes the explanation for the power of these colors is that they symbolize the substances produced by the body: red represents blood, white is milk and semen, and black is for excrement. These three colors all have ambivalent, or inherently contradictory, meanings. Turner goes on to explain that red, white, and black are metaphors for the great milestones in life and the joys and trials associated with them. Red, as the color of blood, signifies sacrifice; white marks sexual maturity; black, as a marker for excrement, is both an emblem of death and regeneration. Since all people have bodies, it is only natural that these colors recur again and again—even in Western cosmetics!

Red is quite clearly the most important and commonly used color for body paint among primitive peoples. Its powerful emotional associations are connected with blood and fire. Among many African tribes, including the Mangbelu of the Congo, red body paint made from palm oil and a paste derived from tree bark is used on numerous ceremonial occasions. Red is perceived as a symbol of life, joy, and health. Red powder is daubed on the face during initiation rites, on the sick, and on the dead as a final mark of respect. Black is consistently associated with more sinister and aggressive types of rituals, mourning, or fertility. White is used as a celebration of the spirits, mourning, or rites of passage.

Body painting is not confined to primitive societies. In the West, the boxer greases his cheeks and breast ceremoniously; supposedly, this is done to "deflect blows." Football players paint black lines under their eyes "to reduce glare." During World War II, men used camouflage paint on their faces. Anthropologist Olivia Vlahos believes that these acts are a symbol of unity, remnants of the ritualistic preparation of a warrior bracing himself for battle; in this way, they are just like the war paint of the American Indian. And, because love is often metaphorically compared to war—it "conquers all," "she fled from his advances," and "he is besieged by admirers"—it is quite understandable why makeup is often playfully termed "war paint."

See also: AMERICAN INDIANS

Breasts

Breasts are mammary glands. In women, they are surrounded by fibrous connective and adipose tissues that account for the breasts' shape. The biological function of the breasts is to secret milk. As such, the breasts are also a significant emblem of femininity in both civilized and traditional societies.

How to Improve the Shape of Breasts. Because of the symbolic emphasis placed on breasts by both men and women, many women experience a great deal of anxiety over the size and shape of their breasts. Size is genetically predetermined. However, some women have reported changes in size as a response to psychotherapy, hypnosis, or hormonal changes brought on by pregnancy, birth control pills, or estrogen treatments.

Venus of Willendorf, an ancient maternity symbol. This motherly figure found in Austria is one of the relics of the Paleolithic Age.

Aside from cosmetic surgery, there are a few steps one can take to improve and maintain the appearance of the breasts. A woman should begin by examining her posture. A drooping chest is often the result of a weak spine and drooping shoulders. Exercise is the best way to prevent or rectify sagging breasts. Any exercises which work the pectoral muscles, including push-ups, swimming, and weight lifting, will help firm the breasts. Sit-ups strengthen the stomach muscles, thereby strengthening the lower back and improving posture. The focused application of pressurized water, or hydrotherapy, is an aspect of beauty care formalized by the French. Hydrotherapy improves both the tone and the shape of the breasts by improving general and local circulation. It should be combined with oil massage daily for a month and then continued once or twice a week for maintenance. Sufficient intake of vitamin C will preserve collagen fibers found in the connective tissue of the breasts.

Cultural Attitudes. The oldest artistic representations of women, which date back to 30,000 to 20,000 B.C. (the Paleolithic age), are statues of huge, buxom females. The Venus of Willendorf, a voluptuous, fetishistic figure found on the shores of the Danube River that dates from approximately 25,000 B.C., is an obvious example of such a symbol of maternity. In addition to representing motherhood, the female breasts have long been a sign of feminine sensuality and served as the focus of erotic treatment. Ancient Egyptian and Roman women gilded their nipples with gold dust.

Breasts go through various changes as a female progresses from infancy to old age. Young girls in a vast variety of cultures await the development of the breasts anxiously as a sign of passage to womanhood. On average, breast buds begin to appear between the ages of nine and eleven. They take eight years to reach full maturity. Nipples begin to acquire pigmentation at age twelve or thirteen. When a woman is pregnant, by the second or third month her breasts begin to tingle and swell as milk is secreted. Gravity eventually causes the breasts to lower and flatten against the rib cage to some extent in later life.

Very few periods have actually celebrated small breasts; one exception is the twenties when the flapper was expected to bind her breasts to create a fashionable flat chested look. Ironically, the cultural periods wherein extremely large breasts were admired were also times defined by sexually repressive attitudes in general. During the Victorian era, corsets emphasized the breasts by reducing the waist and pushing the bosom upward. In the fifties, the supersupport, "torpedo" bra covered by tight sweaters came into vogue, and the American movie screen was dominated by "mammary goddesses" such as Ava Gardner, Jane Russell, and Marilyn Monroe.

Breast Cancer. Fear of breast cancer is widespread among women. Every woman should be aware of the warning signs. The self-examination of the breasts is quite simple. It is best to perform it once a month ten days after the onset of menstruation. Menopausal women should exam their breasts on the same day each month because breasts continue to pass through consistent cycles. Check for lumps, unusual swelling, retraction of the nipple, or bloody discharge. While lying on the back, lift one hand and place behind the head, move the other over the breast in concentric circles toward the nipple, paying especially close attention to the area between the nipple and the armpit where tumors are most common. Switch arms and check the other breast. If anything unusual is detected, seek a medical examination promptly.

The greatest danger from breast cancer is a result of ignoring the body's warnings. Early detection can mean just the removal of the tumor, a relatively minor procedure, instead of the entire breast. In 1843, sixty-four-year-old Countess Rosa Branicka of Poland was diagnosed with breast cancer. She performed an operation on herself and lived to be eighty-two!

Breathing

The Latin word for "breath" is *spiritus;* the same word refers to inspiration from the gods. The English word "respiration" is derived from this Latin word and suggests the deep connection between the sustenance of body and soul. All living cells need oxygen to function. Therefore, breathing represents the spirit of life. In addition to being the means for taking in an important catalyst for life (oxygen), breathing accomplishes the elimination of one third of the toxins produced within the body.

The operation of all organs in the body depends upon the presence of sufficient oxygen in the bloodstream. Aerobic activities—those that help oxygenate the blood—are extremely beneficial. Insufficient oxygen leads to fatigue. Insufficient oxygen in the bloodstream can be caused by many things, including poor posture and certain medical conditions. Most people can quickly exhaust the available oxygen in any unventilated area, especially if walking around. More than thirty minutes in a closed telephone booth would probably result in a blackout.

People generally use only one half of their normal lung capacity. Newborn babies, as is evident to anyone hearing their powerful, hearty cries, have no difficulty breathing deeply. Unfortunately, children unlearn this instinctive skill rather quickly, settling for short breaths that only engage the top of the chest instead of reaching down toward the diaphragm.

Conscious deep breathing is a beneficial method of relaxation. It is also crucial to observe and deepen one's breathing while exercising. Breathe in through the nose and out through the mouth, keeping the lips relaxed and slightly parted. Place a hand on the abdomen to feel it distend. Developing a more efficient use of the lungs leads to a healthier, more radiant complexion as well as increased physical stamina.

Bad Breath. Bad breath, or halitosis, can be both embarrassing and physically uncomfortable. It is often difficult to detect whether or not one has bad breath and, because it is a touchy subject, many people are reluctant to mention it when it is encountered.

The most common reason for bad breath is brushing the teeth too infrequently. When food debris decomposes in the mouth, it emits a sour odor. The best defense is good dental hygiene. However, many instances of bad breath do not originate in the mouth. Bad breath can also occur when bacteria are trapped in the nose, sinuses, throat, and lungs. Halitosis, in these cases, is symptomatic of another ailment. The only cure for bad breath per se is to mask the smell with mints, gum, mouthwash, and toothpaste. It helps to avoid sugar-sweetened products because of the tooth decay they are likely to cause. Apples and cloves are two natural substances that neutralize the breath, thereby combating odor. In the *Kama Sutra*, an old Indian text on erotics and grooming, chewing on betel quid, from a plant which is a member of the pepper family, is recommended for the same purpose. Modern mouthwash is an alkaline liquid that contains alcohol, water, sodium bicarbonate, and flavoring. Mouthwash masks the odor of bacteria found in saliva that is produced during the first phase of digestion. Breath fresheners, available as sprays, accomplish the same end.

Overuse of strong mouthwashes or breath sprays can complicate the initial problem. Other solutions for alleviating chronic bad breath are: stop smoking; drink less alcohol and coffee; and because hunger is one trigger for halitosis, eat light, but more frequent, meals.

Brummell, Beau

In eighteenth century London, Beau (George Bryan) Brummell was among the most influential figures in gentlemen's fashions. He has been described as the king of dandies, and today his name serves as a synonym for any dapper but somewhat foppish man. However, the actual Beau Brummell was a standout in fashionable circles because of his restraint, not his flamboyance. He insisted on scrupulous cleanliness and perfectly tailored clothing. Brummell emerged on the social scene when hygiene was still viewed with suspicion by much of upper class society. His understated style with its stress on subtlety was truly novel during an age of excess.

He never used facial cosmetics. Instead, he scrubbed his face repeatedly every morning to enliven the tone of the skin. He wore and recommended very mild colognes for men. He suggested washing the hair more often instead of powdering it obsessively. Many elaborate rumors were circulated about his "toilette" habits, some of which he himself propagated. Gossip reported that he sent all of his laundry to the country so that it could be aired among fresh flowers. It was also said that he shaved several times daily and then plucked any elusive hairs with tweezers. He frequented three different hairdressers, each of whom he said was responsible for a separate region of his head.

Buttocks

In many societies, buttocks are a symbol of fertility. Women with protuberant buttocks are admired in these cultures. In the West, this region of the body has been artificially accentuated with busties and by the wearing of high heels. The buttocks, which support the weight of a person for long periods of each day, are one of the most neglected areas of the body. The gluteus maximus is potentially a large, powerful muscle, but lack of exercise and overeating often result in its degeneration into a flabby "spread."

C

Catherine De Médici

Catherine de Médici (1519–1589) married Henry II of France and was his queen from 1547 to 1559. After his death and before her own, she was the active governing authority, ruling in her son's name. She had been born into the wealthy and powerful Medici family who ruled Florence during the High Renaissance. The Medicis were noted particularly for their patronage of art and literature. Catherine brought this cultural heritage with her to France and introduced the Parisian aristocracy to many arts, including the ballet.

Catherine herself was a famous beauty, and she was quite proud of it. The walls of her Parisian mansion were lined with over 120 mirrors, and she kept thorough and abundant journals of her cosmetic practices. She poked gentle fun at the efforts of other women whom she encountered on her travels or while holding court. Her diaries mention that her court physician recommended the following for the acquisition of a fair complexion: gather dew-drenched peach blossoms from the royal garden at dawn and crush them with almond oil in the light of the moon!

She and Elizabeth I of England were among the first women to wear flexible corsets. Catherine, who led a very active life designing and supervising the building of elaborate chateaus and even conducting military campaigns during her reign, popularized the corset. She developed the style of riding horseback sidesaddle in order to accommodate her long skirts and tight bodice.

See also: CORSET

Cellulite

Cellulite is lumpy fat resulting from waste buildup in a specific area of the body. It is most common on the hips, thighs, shoulders, upper arms, and back.

Cellulite is different from normal fat as it has greater water content and is more difficult for the body to process and, therefore, eliminate. The fat tissue in cellulite is held together by a network of fibrous adhesions, connective tissue that has hardened abnormally and that will worsen over time. It occurs in portions of the body where circulation is poor due to lack of exercise. It also appears in places where tension has led to chronic muscle spasms. Muscle spasms prevent the proper elimination of wastes and inhibit the flow of blood to the area. Therefore, these areas fail to receive necessary nutrients. The accumulation of wastes results in tissue sludge that in turn creates further blockage.

Aside from a buildup of pollutants in the body, cellulite can also be caused by prolonged stress, long-term use of diuretics, and hormones, all of which may restrict circulation to the lower limbs. Most cellulite begins to develop during periods in a woman's life when she experiences dramatic hormonal changes: in puberty, when starting to use the birth control pill, during pregnancy, and following the first signs of menopause. Irregular secretions from the pituitary gland, the master gland which controls growth, often lead to cellulite developments.

How to Combat Cellulite

Cut down on pollutants such as coffee, alcohol, refined carbohydrates and sugars, and cigarettes. Eat raw, fibrous foods and drink a great deal of water. Cellulite pockets—stagnant regions of the body—can be broken down with intensive massage procedures. Hydrotherapy has also proved successful in treating cellulite and is a principle feature in many European spas. Saunas are another means of clearing debris out of the body and will help speed an anticellulite campaign.

It is important to remember that while cellulite may seem like a mysterious affliction that appears out of nowhere, it is actually a symptom of a holistic body problem. Even if an individual resorts to expensive and painful cosmetic lipasuction, the bumps and puckers of cellulite will reappear unless the life-style that caused them is altered.

Children and Beauty

Prior to the eighteenth century, people believed that children were simply miniature adults. The idea that certain language, environments, situations, and responsibilities were inappropriate for the young did not exist. Children were permitted to drink alcohol, wander through brothels, work in coal mines, and use harsh language. They were also expected to have the same reasoning capacity as adults. Largely through the writings of French philosopher Jean Jacques Rousseau, this attitude began to change. He propagated the notion that people are born free and, because of the pure, pliable state of a child's mind, he or she requires and deserves special treatment in order to flourish. Gradually, most developed countries have sought to preserve the innocence of childhood through such acts as child labor laws.

Along with this respect for childhood innocence, an appreciation for the unique beauty of a child emerged. Children were seen as beautiful by definition, unspoiled and, therefore, sublime. Even in many traditional societies children must reach a certain level of maturity before their bodies are painted for ritual ceremonies. Makeup on a child seems garish, not necessarily because of the cosmetics themselves, but because it creates an image incongruous with the cultural conception of a child's beauty. Both a child's beauty and the art of cosmetics are devalued if they come together too soon.

Child Care and Beauty. Just because most children, especially infants, are perceived as naturally beautiful, it does not mean that there are not some measures for nurturing that raw beauty.

It is crucial to understand beauty in the practical terms of physical well-being. Heredity is the primary factor in any child's beauty potential. However, poor diet, sickness, and various habits may be detrimental to that potential.

In general, healthy parents give birth to healthy children. During potential child-bearing years both adults should be conscious of their nutritional habits. Scientists are demonstrating that what goes inside the bodies from which a third "body" will be produced has more influence than ever suspected.

Theoretically, all children are born with an equal chance for healthy, strong, well-formed teeth and gums. But the neglect can begin to have an effect as early as during gestation in response to the mother's diet. After birth, the high sugar content of much food ingested by the average American child and inadequate tooth brushing quickly reduce a child's initial potential for ideal, beautiful teeth.

Another part of a child's anatomy which suffers early neglect is the feet. A child's feet are not completely formed until the age of fourteen to sixteen. An infant's foot is especially fragile. Strain is placed on these tender feet in three different ways. The first is improper sleeping posture (the fetal position cramps the feet and turns them in; the frog position flattens the arches and turns the feet out). Second, anxious parents may coax a baby to walk before the feet are ready. A baby's internal biological clock will tell him or her when it is time (about six months) to support the weight through standing; no infant needs coaxing. Impatience or eagerness among parents to see their children walk is a result of the old wives' tale that early walking is a sign of superior intelligence; this is not true. Premature weight bearing can only injure the feet, not mark a potential Rhodes scholar. Finally, too much walking on hard, rigid surfaces as the baby is learning to walk can also damage the feet.

The greatest unconscious damage parents do to children's beauty is through sun damage and poor diet. Because the skin of children is more delicate and more easily dried out, it requires even more vigilant protection from the sun. As for diet, although malnourishment plays a significant role, the most obvious manifestations of a poor diet in children is obesity. Aside from the fact that overweight children have more problems as adults with their appearance, they have a statistically shorter lifespan. No child has to be overweight. Childhood weight problems are almost always a function of high fat diets accompanied by copious amounts of refined sugar and a sedentary life-style. Excessive fat cells formed in childhood become permanent, thereby inordinately handicapping the individual when he or she attempts to lose weight as an adult.

Cosmetic products formulated especially for a child's sensitive skin abound: baby lotions, powders, shampoos, massage oils, etc. These range in sophistication from manufacturer to manufacturer. Their high water content and mild chemical components also make these products ideal for adults with sensitive skin. However, many products that claim to be "baby soft" are not so gentle. Avoid products that contain synthetic fragrances, ammonia, and formaldehyde. Children should use extramild, nondetergent, nondeodorant soap. These soaps lather less, but lather has nothing to do with cleaning power. The best soaps are those made of pure olive oil available in natural foods stores.

Cleopatra

Cleopatra was famed as the legendary queen whose beauty captivated such great men as Julius Caesar. She was also noted for her sensitive attention to the cosmetic arts. She even wrote a treatise on beauty care and alchemy. As a cure for baldness, she suggested applying a powder made from red sulphuret of arsenic to the rigorously cleaned bald patches, then removing it with oak gum. She also recommended a skin cream made from seven different oils and geranium petals.

Some literary accounts that describe her experimentation make reference to a supple, green plant with delicate thorns. Reputedly, the queen of the Nile used the juice derived from the leaves of this plant as a cream to protect her skin from the harsh Mediterranean sun. Descriptions of the plant would indicate that it is related to the plant commonly known today as aloe vera, a plant that is, in fact, native to northern Africa.

Cleopatra was proud of her skin and kept it both supple and colorful. While most men and women of ancient Egypt lined their eyes with black kohl, Cleopatra was partial to more vivid colors. Her beauty regimen included painting her upper eyelids blue and her lower lids green. She used white ceruse on her face, neck, and breasts; yellow ochre on her cheeks; and carmine dye on her lips. She also anointed her body with oils made from lion, crocodile, and hippopotamus fat which then required the liberal use of body aromatics, such as perfume.

See also: ALOE VERA

Bathing on the Nile: Cleopatra's Aromatic Formula

- In a cheesecloth bag place a handful of each of the following herbs: rosemary, dried mint, thyme, and lavender. In addition, add one orange peel, one lemon peel, and a tablespoon of lemon pulp.
- Toss the bag into the tub and add very hot water.
- Let seep for ten minutes.
- Allow water to cool for another twenty minutes.
- For a refreshing, tonic, and highly aromatic experience, soak in the tub as long as possible.

Cocoa Butter

This yellowish-white fat derived from cacao seeds was Mae West's favorite beauty aid. Cocoa butter, or oil theobroma, is frequently found in skin products because it works as a natural lubricant and softener. In its natural form, this excellent skin emollient is easy to apply because it melts at body temperature. Many women use cocoa butter on the breasts and stomach during pregnancy because it can arrest the development of striae, or "stretch marks." As they both come from the same source, chocolate and cocoa butter share a similar aroma.

The cocoa bean

Collagen

Collagen is a fibrous protein found in bone, cartilage, and connective tissue (including the skin). It makes up 30 percent of the body's protein and is largely responsible for the youthful appearance of skin and the firmness of muscles.

Biologists claim that collagen molecules are especially susceptible to a phenomenon known as cross-linkage—molecules forming bridges from one atom to another, creating a tangle of fibers and ultimately producing aggregates that enzymes in the body are unable to break down. A cell with tangled fibers becomes crowded and, eventually, its efficiency is hindered. This sluggishness within cells as a result of cross-linkage is associated with the aging process and the formation of wrinkles in particular.

Fiber bunching is caused by exposure to the sun, insufficient vitamins and minerals (most notably vitamin C and zinc), internal stress from physical or mental illness, and exposure to cigarette smoke and pollution. Tangled strands of collagen are also the material that constitutes scars. And, as with scars, collagen can reorganize (thereby smoothing the skin) over time. However, a certain degree of cross-linkage is inevitable, as it appears to be a part of a person's genetic makeup.

Firm, healthy collagen determines the skin's ability to hold water. Dehydrated skin sags and is less capable of eliminating wastes; new cells develop at a slower rate, and the texture of the skin as a whole becomes irregular. There are no easy remedies; protection of collagen involves a holistic, lifelong program of exercise, good nutrition, and a positive, healthy environment. However, with the application of this knowledge it is at least possible to retard the aging process.

Collagen is now used as an ingredient in some skin care products, particularly moisturizing lotions.

Color

The perception of color is actually somewhat subjective and culturally determined. Some languages, as a matter of fact, do not even use separate words for green and blue or for yellow and orange. The Eskimos, on the other hand, have as many as seventeen words for white, all related to different types of snow. While the Japanese consider blue and green to be good and red and purple to be bad, the Western world considers yellow and green as good, red as bad, and purple as a symbol of passion and royalty.

The properties of colors can be used to enhance an individual's unique beauty. Bright colors make the covered area seem larger, and darker, dull colors make the area recede. Some colors, such as bright red and yellow, reflect and thereby bring out these tones in the area surrounding them. Colors also create contrast; brighter colors make light colors seem even lighter. Because colors themselves create a mood, they have come to be associated with specific emotions, e.g., blue with melancholy, green with envy, red with passion, and yellow with cowardice. Mood is a response to the degree of warmth or coolness of a color, which depends on the particular tint, shade, and degree of intensity. Personal beauty can be greatly enhanced by coordinating individual coloring with cosmetics and clothing.

See also: BODY PAINTING, COSMETICS

Complexion

Women in the Middle Ages and the Renaissance went to elaborate efforts to cultivate and preserve pale complexions as a symbol of heightened social status. During this period, only common laborers were forced to submit to the ravages of the sun. "Fair," therefore, meant "pale" as well as "beautiful."

Although, historically, women have been associated with lighter complexions than men, there is no biological predisposition along gender lines for determining skin tone. Nor is the notion that women should possess fairer skin consistently embraced; in the Jewish Orthodox tradition, men with pale skin are admired because it signifies a scholarly life. In India, the caste system is organized in relation to skin tone, lighter skin being associated with aristocracy for both sexes.

Today, in the United States and Western Europe, tanned skin is coveted and cultivated by both sexes. Tanning salons are enjoying a great deal of traffic in spite of evidence that excessive exposure to ultraviolet radiation causes skin cancer and accelerates the aging process. Not too long ago, tanned skin came to symbolize exactly what fair skin once indicated: the leisure associated with the socially well-to-do. The distinction is derived from the fact that the leisure of contemporary society is defined by a more active, as opposed to contemplative, lifestyle—the ability to travel to exotic beaches and pursue challenging and costly recreational sports such as skiing, wind surfing, snorkeling, etc. This trend is beginning to reverse again as information disseminates about the harmful effects of extensive exposure to ultraviolet rays.

The color of the skin is determined by the amount of melanin produced. All human beings possess approximately the same number of melanocytes, the cells which produce melanin. However, in the skins of darker races these cells are more productive. The level of production is largely congenital, but exposure to sunlight stimulates the production of melanin, which is why skin tans. As skin ages, the production of melanin slows, resulting in patches of lighter and darker skin known as age or liver spots.

See also: FRECKLES

Concealers

A concealer is a cosmetic product designed to camouflage darker areas of the skin, such as dark circles below the eyes, blemishes, or patches with irregular pigmentation. Concealers are lighter in color and less transparent than makeup foundation. They are sold in stick or cream form.

The application of concealers requires a light touch and patience. Hurried application just calls attention to the area concealer is meant to disguise. Concealer is best applied with a thin, sable brush. On top, cover the area with a foundation shade slightly lighter than that used on the rest of the face. Blend the two shades gently so that concealer is not removed in the process.

A concealer can also be used along with a blush in contouring— shading to soften or adjust the appearance of facial features. This is done by applying a thin line of concealer under the line of the cheekbone, blending it into the skin with feathery strokes, then applying the blush above.

Conditioners

Hair conditioners are designed to restore the pH balance to shampooed hair and provide greater manageability and strength to the hair. Conditioners should be applied after shampooing the hair, massaged into the scalp, and then rinsed out thoroughly.

The Romans created hair conditioners to combat problems produced by excessive bleaching and dyeing. These first conditioners were made from sheep or bear grease, marrow from deer bones, hellebore (a plant which is a member of the lily family), pepper, rats' heads, and excrement! Luckily, today's products are made with far more appealing ingredients, including many natural aromatics such as aloe, jojoba, chamomile, yucca, and lavender. Beer and eggs are two early hair conditioners that continue to beautify hair today. Conditioners containing balsam or silicone are particularly beneficial to dry or damaged hair as they, like oil treatments, coat the cuticle of the hair, thereby preventing loss of moisture.

See also: BEER, EGG, HAIR MAINTENANCE, pH BALANCE

Corset

A corset is made of stays that are laced together tightly (from whence comes the term "straitlaced") to maintain the body in an upright posture and to exaggerate the proportions of the bust and waist. Twenty to eighty pounds of pressure were required to produce the results mandated by the fashion epitomized by the Gibson girl and stars of the Ziegfeld *Follies*. This is the equivalent of having four hefty volumes of an encyclopedia strapped to either side throughout the day. Corsets were considered essential to the well-dressed woman of a century ago, though a corseted women could barely bend at the waist or breathe deeply. Weakened rib support as the result of prolonged wearing of a corset made it impossible for many woman to support their own weight without the help of a corset.

The design of the corset has varied with changing notions of the ideal form. A form of the corset dates back to the second millennium B.C. These ancient corsets were worn by the Cretans of the Minoan Bronze Age, male and female, as armor. From 1550 to 1660 they were worn to flatten the breasts, and after 1660 to accentuate them. The corset was popularized under the influence of high ranking beauties like Queen Elizabeth I and the Queen of France, Catherine de Médici. The corset fell briefly from grace following the French Revolution when loose, flowing Grecian robes became fashionable. However, corsets returned with a vengeance in 1810, reinforced with whalebone and metal. In 1874, Warners marketed a line of corsets billed as "health items."

The first serious attempt to abolish corsets came in 1908, though most women did not abandon them until after World War I. At this time, women were gradually gaining more freedom as a result of the rising support for women's suffrage and other legal rights; these issues were bravely promoted by early feminists like Elizabeth Cady Stanton, Susan B. Anthony, and Amelia Bloomer (for whom bloomers, an early attempt at designing female pants are named). In 1912, Madame Cadolle of Paris invented and marketed the brassiere and girdle. But the tomboy look of the twenties reinaugurated a corset which again sought to confine the feminine form. In the late thirties, largely due to World War II, the full-figure corset was eliminated. The war effort mandated the diversion of materials such as the metal used to construct corsets, away from the production of luxury items. However, the "merry widow," a simplified boned corset, was popular in the fifties. With the development of inexpensive synthetic elastic fabrics in the sixties, the purpose of feminine underwear became support, not confinement.

Cosmetics

"Beauty is momentary in the mind—
The fitful tracing of a portal;
But in the flesh it is immortal.
The body dies; the body's beauty lives."
—Wallace Stevens

The creation and application of cosmetics is a practice as ancient as prehistory. "Cosmetics" comes from the Greek word *kosmetikos* meaning skilled in adornment. *Kosmetikos* is derived from the word *kosmos*, which means "order." As a means of imposing order on one's body (of changing, or arranging one's outward appearance) cosmetics are an expression of man's desire to contribute order to the natural world.

Prehistoric Origins. The use of cosmetics presumably dates back to 100,000 B.C. Neanderthals used personal adornment as a means of self-protection in a hostile environment. Cosmetics provided camouflage for hunting, a way to stimulate fear, and an expression of spiritual and social concerns. Many anthropologists claim that cosmetics preceded either clothing or jewelry among early Homo sapiens. Body marking and scarification, in which symbols were painted or engraved on the body, were early means of communication and self-expression that may have predated human language. The symbols were worn to protect the person from the fitful forces of nature or to align him or her with a perceived harmonic cosmic order. They made the wearer feel more powerful and less vulnerable to the environment.

Ancient World. The ancient Egyptians used a black substance called kohl as a protection against glare and as the first eye shadow. They used a small implement to draw a dark line which extended to the ear under and above the eye. Hair dyes were made from powdered minerals and plant roots. Henna, still popular today, was a favorite with Cleopatra. Thyme and origanum were major components of fragrant oils, as well as myrrh, frankincense and spikenard which were imported from Arabia.

Aside from sharing its roots with the emergence of a spiritual consciousness in humankind, from the beginning the use of cosmetics was intimately connected with physical well-being. Galen of Pergamum, a Greek physician who is considered the founder of experimental physiology, was the inventor of the first cold cream around A.D. 150.

Romans, who were obsessed with hygiene, perfected the cosmetic bathing ritual, combining washing with exercise, massage, the use of essential oils, and gossip. White lead and chalk were used to whiten the skin. Teeth were scrubbed with pumice, and flour and butter were used to cure pimples and skin eruptions. By A.D. 1100 the use of cosmetics was already widespread in western Europe.

Middle Ages. Women in the Middle Ages subjected themselves to bleedings in order to acquire a fashionable pallor. Some early face powders were made from crushed eggshells mixed with perfume. Red lips were produced by sucking on lemons, which were carried for surreptitious use throughout the day. The crusaders brought home many of the cosmetics used in the Middle East.

Seventeenth and Eighteenth Centuries. Due to their exorbitant costs, cosmetics were used only by the aristocratic classes until the seventeenth century. In the American colonies a stiff luxury tariff and, later, Puritan legal restrictions enacted in a number of states prevented widespread use of cosmetics among the lower classes, youth, and indentured servants. But inevitably, with the increased availability through expanded importation and a market increased by the addition of more female immigrants, attention to cosmetics in all social classes skyrocketed.

Cosmetics attained an age of excess between the mid seventeenth and late eighteenth centuries. In France, women of Louis XIV's court were said to spend as much as twelve hours in preparation for a single ball. Then the French Revolution heralded in a brief reprieve in the use of cosmetics because of their association with great wealth.

In some eras the application of cosmetics became excessively elaborate. As an eighteenth century travel account reports, the beauties of Hanover, a province of northwestern Germany, did not dare sit too close to the fire "lest their complexions melt." Women of the royal courts of Europe often bathed in tubs filled with luxury items such as fresh strawberries. Women and men wore elaborate powdered wigs (some so heavy that the person wearing it had difficulty walking without assistance). The types and use of cosmetic products proliferated during this time. Here are a few of the products which were mass produced:

- *Catchue*—an astringent

- *Chinese Wool* and *French Red*—varieties of rouge

- *Eau de Cologne*

- *Damask Rose Water*

- *Greenough's Tincture*—for preserving teeth and gums

- *Grecian Liquid*—a black hair dye

- *Lady Molyneaux's Italian Paste*—a white cream for coloring hands, face and neck

- *Orange Butter*—for more manageable hair

- *The Right Persian Soap*

- *Royal Milk Bath*—a skin bleach

- *Spanish Papers*—delicate papers imprinted with dye; the forerunner of the compact

Toward the end of the century, personal ornamentation had become so ostentatious that the English Parliament at last decided to take action. In 1770, Parliament enacted a law to impose a penalty on women who used cosmetics "to entrap men into marriage," calling it a form of witchcraft. It remained unenforced, and by the end of the century men were dominating the cosmetic scene, led by the likes of Beau Brummell.

Twentieth Century. As the twentieth century progressed, the variety and accessibility of beauty products became remarkable. In the twenties, elaborate color variations began to appear in the marketplace. Blues, greens, and purples, in addition to traditional black and brown eye shadows, as well as mass-produced nail and hair lacquers were popular. During the Great Depression and World War II, the demand for beauty treatments did not diminish. Glamour was emphasized to boost morale.

Some substances that were actually fatal, such as arsenic and lead, were used in products until as late as 1938, when the federal Food, Drug, and Cosmetic Act was passed to establish standards for consumer protection. Today, manufacturers use in excess of 5,000 ingredients in producing cosmetics. Federal guidelines have had to become more complex as the cosmetic industry has evolved.

The beauty industry profited from wartime scientific advances. Many of the major cosmetic producers occupying the world market today emerged during this time.

Because the war effort put many more women into the workplace, after World War II literature stressing time-saving methods for the task of personal grooming became more prevalent and influenced the type of products manufactured. Also, as the United States became more influential, emphasis on natural-looking beauty emerged. Rosy cheeks and browner skin tones, giving the appearance of an outdoor life, became preferable to a porcelainlike pallor. This desire for subtlety resulted in a demand for more refined cosmetic products.

Women sensitive to the issue took a hand in transforming the industry directly, and the field of cosmetics provided early openings to enterprising and talented women. Even centuries ago, widowed or destitute women took up the trade, working out of their homes to produce toilet water, lotions, soaps, scented candles, powders, and creams. The first black millionaire was an American woman known as Madame J. C. Walker who invented and marketed a method for straightening hair. Many talented, dynamic women have amassed large fortunes as pioneers in the modern cosmetics industry, combining an emphasis on scientific testing with sensitive, alluring marketing techniques.

Cosmetic fashions began to change more and more after World War II. The demand for more and better products continuously increased. In the sixties, many women wished to emulate the look of the French existentialist student with black eye makeup, pale lipstick, and bizarre nail colors such as green, yellow, lavender, blue, or black. Since the seventies, cosmetic fashions have stressed making the most of natural beauty instead of creating a mask that corresponds to a standardized ideal. Today, cosmetics are designed to meet individual beauty needs and problems. This requires taking a more scientific approach to skin and hair care. The priority among both users and makers of cosmetics continues to be the equal, integrated preservation of health and appearance.

Currently, the United States has the largest cosmetic market in the world. Americans spend over seventeen billion dollars annually on cosmetic products. There are more than 1,000 brands of toiletries and cosmetics manufactured by six hundred different cosmetic firms available in the United States. The next largest markets are in Japan, France, the United Kingdom, and West Germany. The consumption and quality of cosmetics is closely related to standard of living. As economic conditions improve in developing countries, more delicately cultivated cosmetics come into demand.

During times of great national crisis, most people experience a decline in standard of living. Luxuries are forfeited and belts are tightened while a concerted communal effort is made to get through the hard times. However, it has been demonstrated statistically that the demand for beauty products, commonly considered luxury items, tends to rise during crisis. (Tattooing also increases in times of crisis!) This was the case in Europe and the United States during the Great Depression and World War II. Demand did not diminish even though a luxury tax was imposed in most countries due to a shortage of petroleum (petroleum being a major component in the manufacture of cosmetics), and a shortage of metal that reduced the container supply.

Lipstick and silk stockings were among the most sought-after black market items in France and England during the war. Because of the scarcity, many women in Europe and the United States painted black lines on the backs of their legs with eyebrow pencils to create the illusion of stockings. Beauty treatments served as morale boosters for women worn down by sacrifice. Concurrently, an interest in male toiletries, which had fallen from favor in the early part of the century due to effeminate connotations, resurged along with a new "masculine" marketing image for such products as after-shave, cologne, and hair cream.

War had other beneficial effects on the beauty industry. Cosmetic surgery improved dramatically during World War I as rehabilitative work was performed on the wounded. Scientific advances made in the process of searching for more efficient means for waging war carried over into the cosmetic industry in the form of improvements in technology and new discoveries in chemistry. Many of the major cosmetic producers occupying the world market today emerged during this time, including Revlon and Chanel.

Cosmetics for Men. Women are not the only ones interested in cosmetics. Throughout history, men have dyed their hair, worn wigs, painted their faces, and manicured their nails. An ordinance passed by the governors of Harvard College in 1636 seeking to curb excess attests that many young fellows were more preoccupied with primping than with scholarly pursuits. The wearing of cosmetics by men did not gain a stigma until the late nineteenth century. Martin Van Buren, a less popular United States president (1837–1841), was ridiculed by many congressmen for his effeminacy and may have contributed to this prejudice.

Applying Cosmetics. According to most professional makeup artists, the essential rule to keep in mind when applying cosmetics for everyday wear is subtlety. This means moderation in both color as well as quantity; it does not mean ignoring detail. The results of overzealous or hurried application can severely detract from an otherwise attractive face. Unlike eras of the past or among primitive peoples, personal adornment in the contemporary West is practiced to complement and heighten natural beauty, not as a symbol in and of itself. Unless the occasion calls for theatrics, makeup should not call attention to itself.

Contemporary cosmetic manufacturers are sensitive to the fact that most women today lead extremely active lives. Very few people can afford to spend hours every day on their appearance, and most women do not have time to reapply their makeup several times daily. This is why it is crucial to approach the first application with care and concentration. An effective way to set makeup on the face in preparation for a busy day is to apply a thin layer of spring water, misted on with an aerosol can. After misting, blot the face gently with a tissue. Long-wear and no-fade cosmetics are available for those with especially strenuous daily routines.

See also: EYELASHES, EYE MAKEUP, LIPSTICK

How to Achieve a Natural Look

- Choose natural, harmonious colors
- Blend well to avoid discernible lines
- Don't over-powder
- Always apply cosmetics on a freshly cleaned face; reapplication without removal can result in a mismatched, patchwork look
- Don't chew or rub the lips, especially when wearing lipstick
- Choose the appropriate makeup for the occasion (for example, bright eye shadows are better for an exotic, evening look)

Cosmetic Surgery

"A defect of the soul cannot be corrected on the face, but a defect of the face, if you can correct it, may correct a soul."

—Jean Cocteau

Cosmetic surgical procedures—also known as plastic surgery—can alter the basic structure of a vast variety of physical features. Operations are available to correct the shape of the ears, nose, mouth, or chin; to remove birthmarks, pockmarks, or wrinkles; to eliminate bags under the eyes; to change breast size; and to change the shape of the body. Each procedure involves varying degrees of pain, expense, and success.

There is nothing fundamentally new about cosmetic surgery. It was being practiced in India at least a thousand years ago. Documentation from medieval anatomists contains warnings about the dangers and complications of performing this kind of surgery. The first famous individual surgeon in this area of expertise, Tagliacozzi, published an elaborately illustrated text describing his procedures in 1597. He was highly successful during his lifetime, but the Catholic church condemned him posthumously for interfering with "God's work." In the nineteenth century, Reverdin, a French surgeon, discovered that a detached flap of skin tissue could continue to thrive in an entirely different portion of the same body.

Annually, 720,000 Americans have surgery just to improve their appearance. Cosmetic surgery is often triumphant in correcting disfigurements that result from accidents, warfare, or some congenital deformities (such as harelips or the saddle nose of congenital syphilis). Loss or lack of facial features has significant psychological repercussions. Plastic surgery can, in these situations, provide salvation.

Dandruff

Dandruff (accumulation of flaky, dead skin cells) is a scalp condition caused by either extreme dryness or excessive oiliness. Dandruff shampoos are designed to encourage exfoliation (the elimination of dead cells from the surface of the skin). The dead cells are then washed away with the shampoo. Products with pyrithione zinc, salicylic acid, and resorcinol rinse away scales, while sulfur and tar slow the reproduction of new cells so that dandruff is arrested.

See also: SKIN, HAIR PROBLEMS

Deodorants

Deodorant products combine aluminum chloride, urea, and other substances to mask the smell of bacteria in perspiration. Most products combine the deodorizing properties with antiperspirants that reduce perspiration by temporarily closing the pores.

The purely negative perception of body odors has only appeared in recent decades and chiefly in the United States. However, this belief and the products it has engendered has several historical links. Although not despising their own scent, all ancient cultures have admired and capitalized on the power of perfume. The widespread—92 percent of all women and 86 percent of all men—use of deodorants in the United

States is a result of the combined legacy of the art of perfumery and the prudery and repugnance toward the body exhibited by the Puritan settlers of America. Americans and Westerners in general are not the only ones who have felt compelled to deodorize the underarms. Native girls from the Trobriand islands in the Pacific rub coconut oil on their armpits to which they adhere flower petals or fragrant leaves.

Anthropologist Margaret Mead has speculated in an interview with Kathrin Perutz that the American obsession with deodorants may also be a result of the vast variety of ethnic groups who inhabit the United States. It is natural for the noses of human beings to behave a bit ethnocentrically. Deodorants provide a means for neutralizing this variation in smell between ethnic groups, not as an annihilation of this difference but as a tool for promoting community in a uniquely diversified culture.

In addition, some psychologists speculate that deodorants may be another means for disguising our mortality to ourselves. A fresh scent is associated with youth, and youth with the spring, the time when flowers bloom. America, itself so young, fears death and decay.

Deodorants/anti-perspirants are now available in creams, sticks, solutions, sprays, and powders.

See also: PERFUME, SENSE OF SMELL

Department Stores

Department stores, modern cosmetics, and fashion have had a parallel and mutually beneficial development. The Bon Marché in Paris is considered the first department store. It began in the nineteenth century as a small shop. The rise of the modern department store in the mid nineteenth century made a range of cosmetic products readily available. In 1867, Altman's department store in New York City announced the opening of the first "making-up" department. The consumer could then experiment with and compare different products, instantly increasing the manufacturers' motivation to improve upon their wares. The first chain stores appeared in the United States in the twenties, making widespread distribution of some items possible.

In addition to convenience and variety, department stores allow the consumer to shop under far more aesthetic and physically pleasing circumstances than in the past. Stores have sought to combine art and utility in a way that makes shopping akin to visiting a contemporary museum. Today, a department store is where much of a culture is on display, where ideas and innovations can be seen and exchanged (both from the shop displays and the people on parade). Formally, 80 to 85 percent of the spending in department stores was done by women. This is gradually changing to a more equitable balance between the sexes.

Depilatory

Depilatories are hair removal products designed to dissolve hair on the surface of the skin. The treatment is not permanent. Some skin types may be sensitive to the chemicals in modern depilatories. Therefore, it is important to experiment on a small area of the skin first. If the intent is to remove facial hair, be certain that the product is specifically designed for that region of the body.

Depilatories are quite ancient. The earliest depilatory creams were made from medicinal plants such as bryony, a vine of the gourd family with large fleshy roots and greenish flowers. In ancient Rome, depilatories were made from a witch's brew of resin, pitch, white vine or ivy gum extracts, she-goat gall, ass fat, bat blood, and powdered viper. The wife of the famous eighteenth century diarist, James Boswell, used dog's urine to remove superfluous hair! Today most depilatories are made with chemicals and can be purchased in a drugstore or pharmacy.

White Bryonia

Dermabrasion

Dermabrasion is the surgical procedure of scraping off upper layers of the skin with a planing device in order to remove or reduce acne scars, pockmarks, and tattoos. The first time it is performed, the appearance of the skin will usually show 30 to 60 percent improvement. Severe cases may require several abrasions. The surgeon removes the outer layers of skin with a high-speed rotary wheel that has a stone, wire brush, or diamond fraise cover. Usually, dermabrasion is an in-office procedure, but sometimes it does involve hospitalization. Initially after the operation, the results are unsightly. A yellow ooze appears on the surface of the tender new skin. It forms a crust that peels. This cycle repeats for approximately two weeks. For about two months the skin remains reddish and extremely sensitive. One should avoid the sun at all costs during this time.

See also: COSMETIC SURGERY

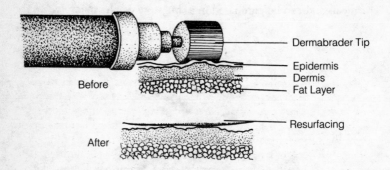

Cross section of the skin before and after dermabrasion

Dermatitis

Dermatitis refers generally to an irritation of the skin. Contact dermatitis, specifically, is an allergic reaction caused by cosmetic products among other substances. According to the federal Food and Drug Administration, the highest rate of allergic reactions are caused by deodorants and antiperspirants, hair sprays, hair coloring products, bubble bath, mascara, moisturizers, eye creams, and chemical depilatories.

People who are allergic, or suspect they might be sensitive to a particular product, should start with a patch test before using a product regularly. Most department stores and even some drugstores display samples of products that can be tested before a purchase is made.

Today, the FDA carefully monitors the manufacture of cosmetic products to ensure consumer safety. Increased technology and consumer awareness have engendered a heightened sense of responsibility on the part of cosmetic manufacturers to respond to the needs of allergy-prone consumers.

See also: ALLERGENS

E

Earrings

As with most personal adornment, ear piercing is practiced to reflect status and to attract the opposite sex. With the notable exception of the Puritan era, earrings have been worn by most cultures across the globe and throughout history. However, the particular popularity of pierced ears in Western culture may have received indirect reinforcement from old English superstitions. English sailors used to believe that an earring worked as protection against drowning. The general population also subscribed to the pierced ear as a cure for vision problems. The punk—the angry youth who emerged in financially stagnant Britain during the nineteen seventies—fortified ear piercing in an odd way. Punks proudly display their ferociousness with as many as ten holes in a single ear, not to mention safety pins penetrating the cheek and lips. What began as a political statement has penetrated the world of fashion.

Nowadays earrings are once again worn by both sexes, although men in Western culture generally limit themselves to one modest piece of jewelry in one ear. Earrings designed for women continue to evolve and expand in variety, reflecting the influence of outside cultures and the multifarious nature of fashion in the late twentieth century.

Ears

The ears are the auditory organs of the body. They transform sounds into electrical impulses and send them to the brain for translation. The squashed trumpet (the outer ear) located on the sides of the head does very little of the actual processing work. The major function of the outer ear is to work as a filter and aid in determining the direction of sound. The shape of the human ear is a poor substitute for the sensitive, mobile catchment cups of many other mammals.

Another perplexing feature of the outer ear is the earlobe. Although many scientists have dismissed the earlobe as obsolete to humans in their current evolutionary state, the keen sensitivity of this tiny area continues to attract attention. Anthropologist Desmond Morris claims that this sensitivity is itself an evolutionary development, the emergence of another erogenous zone. He believes this occurred as a result of the fact that humans, unlike animals, prefer to couple face-to-face. Since human sexual activity is also continuous, rather than seasonal like other mammals, the face has considerable sexual significance. This may explain why in ancient accounts as well as contemporary surveys most people express displeasure with protruding ears yet admire a sizable earlobe. Suya peoples of Brazil emphasize the ear in body symbolism; ear discs and rings are supposed to help make one's sense of hearing more acute and allow one to better "know things."

Certainly, humans have not overlooked the ears' possibility for drawing focus to and setting off the face. The earlobe is a popular site of ornamentation. It is common among many cultures to apply scent behind the ears and pierce the ears for jewelry.

See also: EARRINGS, OTOPLASTY

Eating Disorders

Eating disorders are illnesses of both mind and body. Gluttony, intentional starvation, and self-induced vomiting are not new. The ancient Romans of the upper classes reputedly vomited between courses at large banquets, and Roman women were given to starving themselves in trying to attain an "ideal" figure. However, the medical community has only recently made the link between obsessive eating behavior and deep-seated problems of self-image.

Two syndromes that have earned a great deal of attention in recent decades are bulimia nervosa and anorexia nervosa. These two ailments are far more common among females than males. The victims of these illnesses are generally in their mid to late teens and are consumed by a morbid fear of becoming fat, an obsession that becomes the foremost focus of their thoughts. Weight and self-esteem are completely entangled.

Bulimia means "overeating" and it involves binges on high-calorie foods. A loss of control defines these binges, which end in self-induced vomiting, sleep, abdominal pain, or "getting caught." Depression and a lowered self-image accompanies the period following binges. Frequent and noticeable fluctuations in weight characterize the bulemic. Bulimia is often a symptom of anorexia nervosa.

Anorexia seems to arise out of insecurity about family relationships, personal identity, sexual development, and work. Aside from deep-rooted dissatisfaction with self and with life in general, the anorexic is usually a perfectionist. A thinner body becomes the obsessive symbol of success. Initial weight loss generates compliments, and dieting efforts are then doubled and eventually carried to the point of starvation. The anorexic is deaf to the pleas of family members and friends to eat more. Even after wasting away to a mere skeleton, she will still insist that she is overweight. Many anorexics become so malnourished that they require hospitalization. In treating anorexics, doctors first restore their weight to a healthy level and then use psychotherapy to raise their self-image and uncover the problems that predisposed them to the illness. About 10 percent of all American girls between the ages of thirteen and eighteen believe they have symptoms of anorexia. Researchers believe that the increase in eating disorders is to some degree a function of modern society's idolization of thinness as the standard for personal beauty. However, it is clear that bulimics or anorexics are vulnerable individually as well as culturally.

Eating disorders follow the pattern of addiction, and some researchers believe that food (like drugs or alcohol) is used as a substitute for what is missing from life or to mask forgotten childhood abuse. A complete profile of the individual most likely to develop an eating disorder has yet to be constructed. It is clear that obsessive dieting leads to an obsession with hunger. The reaction to this obsession can be seen in either of two behaviors: gorging or fasting. If self-control in the face of food becomes synonymous with goodness and any deviation is perceived as wicked, a vicious cycle of guilt is established. Beauty and self-worth are codependent. Reducing them to the painfully simplistic equations of "thin is good" and "fat is bad" cripples both the mind and the body.

Egg

It has been suspected for at least a thousand years by people in various cultures that eggs have some value for increasing the natural sheen of hair. This has now been confirmed by scientific testing in the cosmetologist's laboratory. The egg yolk contains vitamin A and D, vitamins that promote a healthy complexion and disease resistance in general. Because eggs provide a source of protein and hair is made of protein, one egg per day as a regular part of the diet will produce results. Eggs (yolks, whites, or whole) can also be used as a facial mask. Such a mask will soften lines and smooth wrinkles. In terms of external beauty, the cholesterol in eggs is actually beneficial; it rejuvenates the oil-producing cells in the skin.

See also: BEER, CONDITIONERS

How to Use an Egg Rinse

- Beat one raw egg. (You may wish to use only yolks or whites if that is what is on hand after doing some baking.)
- Either mix the egg into the shampoo you are about to use or add it to the hair after shampooing.
- Rinse thoroughly with cool water.

How to Use an Egg Mask

- Beat one raw egg.
- Apply to the face and neck.
- Lie down for one hour, keeping the facial muscles as relaxed as possible.
- Rinse with cool water.
- Repeat weekly for a noticeably softer complexion.

Egypt

Scholars date ancient Egyptian dynasties as early as 4500 B.C. Concrete evidence of highly developed culture dates nearly as far back. Specifically, archaeologists and anthropologists who are engaged in the study of the architecture, language, and customs of ancient Egypt have found vast evidence pertaining to the cultivation of beauty. From the artifacts of this civilization, one might speculate that the ideal female beauty possessed lustrous, abundant hair, deep-set, dark blue eyes, large breasts, and full lips.

Several specific examples of the Egyptian contribution to the art of beauty culture exist, some of which remain with us today. The ancient Egyptians buried their deceased royalty in the finest raiments and in tombs encased with priceless jewels. In addition, archaeologists have unearthed small clay pots (some dating back as far as 3000 B.C.) which contain ancient samples of makeup. Elaborate combs and mirrors have also been retrieved from tombs. The Egyptians believed that beautiful enshrinement ensured a warm reception in the afterlife because the gods smile favorably on a beautiful human form.

The most notable characteristic of Egyptian sculpture and wall paintings is the striking eyes, an effect which was probably achieved on living women of the day with these beauty aids. Men, women, and children all used a black substance called kohl as a protection against glare and as the first eye shadow. They used a small wooden or ivory stick to draw a dark line extending to the ear under and above the eye.

Egyptian royalty, both male and female, would shave their entire heads and wear wigs of spiraling curls made from human hair, palm leaf fiber, and wool which were dyed bright red or ebony. The less privileged members of society wore wigs made of felt. Depilatories used to remove body hair also originated in ancient Egypt and are frequently mentioned in *The Arabian Nights*. Masks for nurturing the skin of the face were made from such diverse substances as clay, meat, eggs, and pulverized water lilies.

Smooth skin was greatly admired and, due to the heat of the climate, clothing was considered superfluous for centuries. Although the Egyptians did not need to apply their imaginations to the development of elaborate dress, the upper strata of society, particularly the royal household, clothed their bodies with perfumes, oils, and jewels. The range of olfactory stimulants the Egyptians produced is remarkable. To quote Shakespeare on Cleopatra, "The barge she sat in . . . so perfumed that the winds were love-sick with them," (*Antony and Cleopatra*). Indeed, the entire civilization on the Nile was reputed to be as aromatically intoxicating as this description suggests. The Egyptians also took personal hygiene very seriously. They built a bathing system that was later adapted by the Greeks and Romans. The foundation of Western beautification practices was first established in Egypt.

See also: COSMETICS

Electrolysis

Electrolysis is the most well-known hair removal procedure available today. It is offered as a special feature at some beauty salons or at clinics established solely for this purpose. The general procedure involves the use of electrodes that are placed into hair follicles with needles. The electrodes discharge a high-speed electric current, destroying hair at the root.

There are actually two kinds of electrolysis. Galvanism destroys hair by decomposing the papilla (the hair's source of nourishment), and it involves multiple needles. Galvanism is the older of the two methods; it is slower but it has nearly a 100 percent rate of success. Diathermy is faster (and more common today), but it requires more skill to perform and has 20 percent regrowth rate. In short-wave diathermy, an electric current generates a heat reaction within the hair follicle; this kills hair at the root using one well-placed needle.

While electrolysis is the only genuinely permanent means for accomplishing the removal of unwanted hair, it is expensive, time consuming, and somewhat painful. If the technician is inexperienced and careless, electrolysis can leave scars. Before considering electrolysis, it is wise to experiment with other semipermanent hair removal products such as hot wax or depilatories, or use bleach to lighten the hair. Consult a physician if serious questions arise or the problem is severe; if the excess hair is the result of a hormonal imbalance, prescription drugs may be necessary. If the decision to invest in electrolysis persists, choose a technician who is both experienced and inspires confidence.

Elizabeth I, Queen of England

Aside from being one of the most powerful and well-respected British rulers in history, Elizabeth I (1533–1603) was also noted for her great beauty. However, several of her cosmetic routines would seem quite peculiar to the modern woman. She used a pomade made from dog fat and apples to smooth her radiant, fine red hair. She shaved the front of her hairline to emphasize her high forehead. She painted the veins of her breast (which the fashions of the period exposed) blue to emphasize the paleness of her skin.

During the Renaissance in Europe when Elizabeth ruled (1558–1603), most people regarded bathing with great suspicion. An understanding of the beneficial side of personal hygiene was just beginning to emerge. Those of the enlightened elite boasted that Elizabeth bathed once a month "whether she needed it or no."

Sadly, her beauty did fall upon hard times; later in her life dignitaries from abroad reported that her teeth had turned entirely black and her near-baldness required her to wear a wig.

Emulsifiers

Emulsifiers are an important ingredient in lotions. They enable the mixing of oil and water, two substances that normally will not blend. Emulsifiers are technically soaps and they work with stabilizers or binders (gums), coating the microscopic globules of either oil or water with a thin film to keep water- and oil-based ingredients together. This way, active ingredients are uniformly dispersed throughout a solution. A stable emulsion can hold up to 90 percent water. Sodium lauryl sulfate is a common emulsifier.

Essence

The word "essence" comes from the Latin word *esse* which means "to be." In chemical terms, an essence is a concentrated extract derived from a substance. In this concentrated form, all of the most important and fundamental qualities of the source are retained. A true perfume is composed primarily of the essence of one of a wide variety of plants.

Essential oils are derived from various parts of plants: flowers petals, bark, leaves, roots, or wood. Some plants whose oils are commonly used in the manufacture of perfume include geranium, jasmine, lavender, cinnamon, citronella, rose, patchouli, sandalwood, rosemary, lily, violet, and tuberose.

Essences are removed from the plant at the prime of its life. At this point, the essences look more like water than oil, and like water are absorbed quickly into the skin. Essential oils contain powerful vitamins and enzymes that in part account for their healing properties. However, the component parts of essential oils do not entirely explain their success in both beauty and health care. Essential oils work holistically; that is, the whole seems to be greater than the sum of its chemical parts. This is why synthetic oils that have exactly the same chemical components fail to have the same qualities and potency.

The essential oils of a fragrant flower come from baglike structures called sacs. The process of extracting oil from flower petals is delicate and costly. Three different methods are employed to accomplish this task:

1. Steam distillation—steam is passed through the plant. The essential oil converts to a gaseous state, which is then channeled through tubing, cooled, and returned to a liquid state.

2. Solvent extraction—petals are dissolved in a solvent. This solvent is then extracted, leaving behind a waxy residue that contains the oil. The wax is then dissolved in ethyl alcohol that causes the essential oil to rise to the top. Through the application of heat, the alcohol evaporates and leaves behind a highly concentrated form of the essential oil.

3. Enfleurage—flower petals are placed upon a layer of fat resting on a glass plate. Oil from the petals is absorbed into the fat. A greasy pulplike material forms, which is treated with alcohol, and then the oil can be dissolved out.

See also: AROMATHERAPY, PERFUME

Exercise

In this age of health consciousness, most people in developed Western nations are aware of the need for regular exercise. However, 64 percent of Americans between the ages of six and seventeen cannot pass a basic fitness examination. Being beautiful and being physically fit are synonymous in contemporary society. Exercise also helps combat depression, and people in good physical condition tend to sleep less and more deeply.

However, many people become quickly discouraged when embarking on an exercise program because they fail to understand a few basic anatomical principles. Overexertion leads to sore muscles and possible injuries, which in turn inhibits further exercise. The beginner is not a trained athlete and should not act like one. One should build up a routine by carefully attending to the body's signals.

If it communicates exhaustion, stop. Those who are overweight should begin slowly, building up stamina gradually. No matter how fit, those who exercise should always do a series of warm-up stretches before turning to more strenuous exercise. Stretches elongate the muscles, while other forms of exercise shorten and tighten them. This is why it is important to stretch before and after other isometric, aerobic, or calisthenic exercises.

Isometric Exercise. Isometric exercise involves the application of pressure. One set of muscles is tensed in opposition to another set or an immovable object for a period of a few seconds. The procedure is repeated in short series. Weight lifting is an example of isometric exercise.

Aerobic Exercise. Aerobic exercise burns calories and increases the heart rate. As the heart pumps faster, the amount of oxygen taken in and distributed throughout the body increases; this leads to a stronger and more efficient body in general—better digestion, more energy, and a sturdier heart. Recent evidence demonstrates that aerobics can even improve memory, reasoning ability, and reaction time. Doctors and fitness instructors recommend thirty minutes of sustained aerobic exercise three times weekly. Some forms of aerobic exercise are swimming, jogging, jumping rope, dancing, and brisk walking.

Calisthenics. Calisthenics are traditional exercises for firming the body such as sit-ups, push-ups, jumping jacks, and chin-ups. They combine the objectives of isometric and aerobic exercise.

An overwhelming variety of exercise programs are now available in the form of classes, videos, manuals, etc., not to mention the classic options of martial arts, dance, structured team sports, weight lifting, swimming, and jogging. The chief priority is to suit the program to the individual and make a decision based on what feels good, is inspiring, and does not require an excessive amount of psychic manipulation to get motivated. Joining clubs or committing to classes often helps the person who lacks self-discipline. In any case, try to avoid unrealistic goals while working at every session toward slight improvement.

Exercise Tips

- Wear loose, absorbent clothing.
- Drink water as needed before, during, and after.
- Allow forty-eight-hour intervals between workouts so that muscles can recuperate.
- Invest in good exercise shoes.
- Do not eat immediately before exercising.

Eye

"For where is any author in the world
Teaches such beauty as a woman's eye?"
—Shakespeare, *Love's Labour's Lost*

"And looks commercing with the skies,"
Thy rapt soul sitting in thine eyes."
—Milton, "Il Penseroso"

The eye is a specialized sensory organ for sight that receives light rays and transmits them as electrical signals to the brain. These signals are interpreted as visual images by the brain. The tissue of the eye contains millions of light receptors.

But the eyes do more than process the light that is reflected onto them. They also reflect the inner self back out to the world. They are the most expressive feature on the face. The eyes are a powerful means of communication revealing the extent of a person's sincerity, honesty, passion, and sexual or intellectual interest in another person. The eyes communicate complex, unspoken messages. The ability to look unflinchingly into another's eyes is a sign of confidence and an invitation to further intimacy. Curiously, women tend to look directly into the eyes of another more readily than males do.

Eye Shape. Just as an astrologer believes that a map of the stars at the hour of a person's birth reveals much information about his or her disposition, physiognomists used to believe that the shape of the human eye indicated certain personality traits: medium-sized eyes marked a pragmatic nature; large eyes signified the observant, adventurous individual; small eyes showed the potential for keen concentration; close-set eyes indicated a skeptic and a possible "operator"; and eyes set far apart belonged to the reliable, trustworthy soul. These claims carry little weight in the modern world. However, one fact about eye shape is certain. On the average, even across racial lines, the eyes of women are larger, more susceptible to shadows on the lids and just below the eyes, and have longer and stronger lashes initially than those of men.

Eye Color. In much Western literature and folklore, blue eyes are associated with goodness and a gentle nature while dark eyes signify passion and sensuality. To Moslems, however, gray eyes are a sign of amorality and cowardice. Eye color generally follows hair color, although there are vast numbers of exceptions. Interestingly, all of the many shades of eye color are derived from a single brown pigment known as melanin. The specific shade—green, blue, brown, or black—is a result of the abundance or lack of melanin in the iris. A lack of melanin is why lighter eyed persons experience greater difficulty seeing in bright sunlight.

Egyptian hieroglyph depicting an eye

Symbolic Meaning. The eye is a powerful symbol in many cultures. The eye was an important hieroglyphic device in ancient Egypt and signified the sun gods, symbolizing the power and perfection of the sun. The earliest seafaring people painted the image of a human eye on the front of their ships as a protection in troubled seas. Bartlett's *Familiar Quotations* contains over 350 entries under "eye(s)" including "Keep me as the apple of the eye" (Bible); "With affection beaming in one eye, and calculation shining out of the other" (Charles Dickens); and "One's eyes are what one is" (John Galsworthy). For the Trobrianders of the western Pacific eyes are "the gateways of erotic desire." Carl Jung, the successor to Sigmund Freud, called the eye the archetypal symbol in dreams and art, standing for "the rest and peace of the maternal bosom." The English language is sprinkled with metaphorical expressions involving the eyes: "an eye for an eye," "catch your eye," "feast one's eyes." The eyes as the "mirror(s) of the soul" reveal the true nature of a human being. No other organ combines so many attributes—utility, motion, self-maintenance, delicacy, clarity, strength, and beauty.

Eye in Art. The human eye also plays an important role in both poetry and religion as a metaphor for the sun, the stars, the mind, spirituality, alertness, and the penetrating nature of justice. The goddess Mari of ancient Syria had huge eyes that could see into men's souls; Dante's Beatrice reflected the light of Paradise in her eyes. The Medusa of Greek mythology, who could turn men into stone with her gaze, represents another interpretation of the powerful glance. Mythology, folklore, and poetry warn against the curse of the "evil eye" (a cross-cultural phenomenon) and the seductiveness of "bedroom eyes" almost as frequently as they praise the splendor of "soulful eyes." Shakespeare compares a woman's eyes to Promethean fire. As told in Greek mythology, Prometheus stole fire from the gods as a gift for humanity which resulted in their rapid development and simultaneous alienation from the divine. This metaphor encapsulates the paradoxical responses generated by the enchanting lure of the human eye. While beautiful eyes can inspire and delight, they can also lead an undiscriminating beholder to poor judgment or loss of self. This paradox has been expressed throughout the centuries in the form of wary skepticism. According to a sixteenth century madrigal by Thomas Morley, she may have "July in her eyes," but "in her heart a cold December." With eyes, as with all subjects of mythic tales, the distinction between good and evil powers is often elusive.

The significance placed upon the human eye also explains the attention women (and, in many cases, men) around the world pay to heightening the effects of this expressive component of human anatomy. Cleopatra painted her upper eyelids blue and her lower lids green. Nero used black kohl to create catlike eyes in imitation of the pharaohs of ancient Egypt. In the seventeenth century as well as in ancient Rome, it was popular to deposit the juice of belladonna, a European plant which is the source of atropine (a poisonous crystalline alkaloid), into the eyes to increase their brilliance and dilate the pupils. Today a remarkable variety of shades, textures, and consistencies of cosmetics for the eye are available. Some people wear colored contact lenses to brighten or actually alter the natural color of their eyes.

Health. While accentuating the natural charms of the eyes, it is important to nurture the eye itself. While most older civilizations, such as ancient Greece, revered the blind as prophetic seers, many less fortunate persons throughout history who were blind, walleyed, or cross-eyed were marked as witches or the victims of satanic possession. Now modern science teaches that the eyes are an important indicator of physical health, a mirror of the body as well as the soul. Jaundice, a condition resulting from bile pigments in the blood, turns the eyes yellow; a jaundiced condition can indicate hepatitis or other serious problems of the liver or kidneys. Eye examinations can also reveal otherwise unsuspected diabetes, brain tumors, hemorrhage, abscess, syphilis, parasites, an overactive thyroid gland, and anemia. Red eyes can be an indication of allergies, fatigue, sleeplessness, excessive alcohol intake or other drug abuse, or exposure to harsh chemicals or polluted air.

In eighteenth century England, rubbing sore eyes against a black cat's tail was considered a cure. While this superstition is another example of the primordial connection between the human eye and spiritual powers, it would hardly inspire confidence today. A more effective home remedy is one that dates back to the lore of medieval herbalists. The fennel plant (*Foeniculum vulgare*), a tall herb of the carrot family with yellow flowers, contains medicinal seeds that smell like licorice. Seeping a teaspoon of fennel seeds in hot water creates a soothing eye bath. Of course, a number of effective commercial products are now available. Many of these products are made with boric acid. Boric acid acts as a mild antiseptic for red or itchy eyes while flushing pollutants from the eye. More serious conditions call for prompt consultation with a physician.

Because the eyes serve as a major filter between an individual and the world, it is important to treat them well. Although it is something of an old wives' tale that reading fine print in dim light strains the eyes, it is nonetheless true that the eyes can be overworked. Persons whose occupations entail extended, concentrated use of the eyes should work toward maintaining a state of visual relaxation, avoiding squinting, and periodically allowing the eyes to rest by focusing on a solid black surface. Rinse tired or strained eyes with a prepared solution. When removing cosmetics, use products specifically designated for eye makeup removal as they are made with substances that will not injure this sensitive region of the face. Remove all makeup thoroughly and carefully before going to bed; residue can get into the eyes as one sleeps so that it is possible to rise from a full night's rest with bloodshot eyes. Excessive use of tobacco can impair the central (as opposed to the peripheral) vision. Extended TV viewing can strain the eyes (one hour of television is equivalent to two and a half hours of movies in terms of eye fatigue). To reduce the harmful effects of considerable exposure to television one should avoid sitting too close to the screen and refrain from watching in total darkness.

For most people, the eyes hold up throughout a lifetime of use, even overuse. But as a further preventive eye care measure, both optometrists and cosmetologists acknowledge the value of exercising the eye (e.g., conscious blinking and rolling of the eyes) in order to strengthen the muscles. The fact that eyes require exercise explains why the extended use of eyeglasses, which act as a supportive crutch for impaired vision, gradually weaken the eye muscles and result in a worsening of the original condition. Exercising the eyes also tightens the skin below the eyes where persons are most likely to develop their first wrinkles. Because the pupils of the eye dilate involuntarily in response to excitement and contract in response to unpleasant sights or thoughts, in the interest of greeting the world with bright, wide eyes it is important to gaze with enthusiasm!

Eyebrows

The eyebrows play an important role in the expressiveness of the face. For this reason, folklore has ascribed characteristics to persons with different shaped brows (just as it has with other facial features). Brows that meet in the middle are supposed to mean hardheartedness in men and jealousy in women; those set far apart indicate frigidity; those close to the eyes suggest gravity; long brows indicate a sage; and those raised high above the eyes mark the timidly inquisitive. Although there is no rational basis for these claims they do demonstrate an awareness of the significance the brows play in forming facial expressions and adding character to the face.

Plucking and shaving eyebrows has gone in and out of fashion. Eyebrow tweezers are the most common cosmetic implement throughout the world. During the Renaissance many women shaved off their entire brows in order to heighten the appearance of a smooth, alabaster complexion and in England this was perceived as a tribute to the beauty epitomized by their queen, Elizabeth I. Today, due in part to the look characteristic of such models as Brooke Shields and Mariel Hemingway, naturally dark, thick brows are in vogue. The "perfect" eyebrows are those sculpted to balance with the other features of the face.

The functional purpose of the eyebrow provides a shade for the eyes from sunlight and a filter for ambient dust. Aesthetically speaking, the eyebrows frame the face, and as with a frame chosen to complement a fine painting, makeup artists recommend that eyebrows be shaped to accord with the proportions of the face.

The decision to pluck the eyebrows to any dramatic extent should be contemplated carefully, as the hair of the brows grows back much more slowly than the hair of the head. Each follicle spends only ten weeks actively growing, followed by a nine month rest period.

Before beginning to tweeze the brows, clean the area around the eyes thoroughly. With a finger, brush the brows in both directions to remove any loose hairs. Apply a small amount of moisturizer to this surface. Rub tweezers with a cotton ball dabbed with alcohol or another astringent. Remove stray hairs that are clearly extraneous and detract from the desired line. The hairs should be plucked in the same direction the hair grows; pull from the root, not the end. When plucking is complete, apply a toner or astringent to the brows and refrain from applying makeup to this surface for at least thirty minutes.

Eyebrow pencils, used to intensify the brows, should be a shade lighter than the natural color of the brow hair. Often it is best to use two different shades, unless brows are black, in order to achieve the most natural look. Brush the brows backward, apply light, feathery strokes in the direction opposite to that in which the hair grows, then brush the hairs back over the strokes. This way the lines will be virtually indistinguishable from the natural hairs. To achieve a deeper hue as a substitute for or complement to cosmetics, brows and lashes can be dyed. The effects of this process generally last for a few months.

Eyelashes

The eyelashes, or cilia, are small hairs extending from the cells surrounding the eyelids. Together with the eyebrows, they form an important protective fringe designed to filter the amount of light that enters the eye and protect it from alien particles. The lashes on the upper lid are longer and more abundant than those on the lower lid. A person has approximately 200 total eyelashes, and each lash lasts three to five months. Eyelashes continually replace themselves throughout a lifetime. They do not lighten with age although they do lighten in the sun. Women and many men have darkened their eyelashes artifically as a means of beautification since at least the time of the pharaohs in ancient Egypt.

See also: EYE MAKEUP

Eyelid Correction Surgery

Blepharoplasty, or eyelid correction surgery, is a form of cosmetic surgery often performed in conjunction with a face-lift. An incision is made through one of the crow's feet and an ellipse of skin is removed from the upper lid and a small strip from the lower. Pockets of fatty tissue situated below the lower lid are also removed to remedy bags under the eyes. When the surgeon has carefully examined the eyes to ascertain that the corrections are symmetrical, the incisions are sutured with nylon or silk threads. The act of making the incision and removing just the right amount of skin is tricky, however.

See also: COSMETIC SURGERY

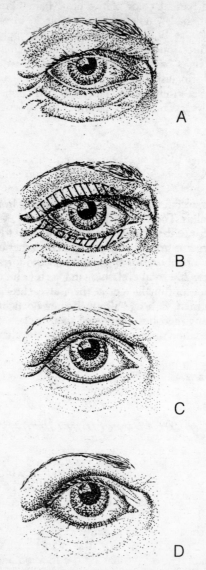

Eyelid correction surgery. Illustration A shows both the eyelids before the surgical correction. In figure B, the parts which will be removed are indicated. Skin and fat are removed and the wound is sutured. Figure C shows the almost invisible scars. Figure D shows the final result.

Eye Makeup

Cosmetics designed to enhance the beauty of the eyes include eye liners, eye shadows, concealers, and mascara. Eye shadows come in a vast array of colors from natural tones and highlighters to highly dramatic and exotic shades.

When purchasing eye makeup, check to see that the products contain preservatives. Most eye cosmetics have special preservatives which greatly reduce the odds of a bacterial invasion of the eye. As a further preventive against infection or inflammation, always wash hands before applying eye makeup; hands pass on more germs than an exchange between mouths. Also, avoid sharing with others cosmetics that are applied by hand. Keep eye makeup containers tightly closed. Never lick or spit on an eye makeup brush. Keep eye makeup out of the sun; heat kills the preservatives.

Eye Liner. While heavy eye liner is no longer fashionable, subtly applied liner is useful for slightly altering the shape of the eye. To make the eye appear to slant up instead of down start a line in the center of the upper eyelid. Do not bring the line all the way to the edge of the eye; instead, extend the line slightly upward. Black women should use a dark blue liner; persons with other skin tones should use brown or gray. Black is appropriate only for very large, dark eyes.

Eye Shadow. The contrast between the white and the iris of the human eye accounts for the eye's expressiveness. This is why if sickness or fatigue dim or redden the whites of the eye, the most vivid eye can go unnoticed. Eye shadows are designed to heighten the natural palette of the eye. They accentuate the play of shadow and light by creating a second level of contrast. Because the eyes are the most expressive part of the human face this seemingly fanciful practice is actually quite rational.

Tinting the eyelids originated in the East. The first shades were exclusively dark and were made from crushed minerals. Malachite and galena (a dark gray lead ore) were ground on a stone slab, then stored in shells, hollow reeds, and alabaster vases. Almost all Egyptians, men and women, adults and children, used black kohl, similar to *alchole* used by the Turks centuries later. The shadow was applied with wooden or ivory sticks. Early glitter shades were made from fish scales. Colored shades came into vogue much later and were popularized during the twenties by the bold flapper. In the nineteen fifties, with the influence of Oriental and Egyptian models, the cat-eye look was coveted. The nineteen sixties saw the simultaneous inauguration of a more natural look and the brightest ever blue eye shadows. Today the variety of colors manufactured is diverse enough to satisfy the most experimental face painter. When used in tandem with theatrical evening wear, vivid colors can create a glamorous look, but for normal occasions, shades that complement rather than overwhelm natural eye color are best. Pale lavender on black skin and shades of brown or beige on lighter skin create the most natural look. The shade should be selected to blend with the color of the natural shadow located between the bridge of the nose and the inner corner of the eye.

Eye shadows come in four forms: powders, creams, sticks, and liquids. Powders should be applied with a sable brush, and creams and sticks should be applied with a fingertip. Liquid shadows generally are sold with an applicator. A paler shade (usually cream) should be applied as a highlighter to the prominent bone that projects just below the eyebrow. This widens the appearance of the eye. Carefully blended concealers applied below the eyes can cover dark circles. Products are also available to moisturize and firm this delicate area.

Mascara. The word "mascara" is derived from the Italian *maschera* ("mask") and the French word *masca* ("witch"). Despite the negative connotations this latter-day etymology may suggest, mascara has been a coveted cosmetic for thousands of years. Some of the most ancient civilizations—Egypt, Mesopotamia, Sumeria, Greece, and Rome—used kohl not only as eyeliner but also as mascara. A more refined form of mascara was introduced in the United States during the Civil War by a European empress. Shortly after World War II, Helena Rubinstein was the first to reduce mascara to the size of a fountain pen, making it easy to carry in a purse and apply on the go.

Contemporary mascara is made with purified water and insoluble ingredients such as lanolin and paraffin. The black color is obtained from iron oxides and carbon. The preservatives in mascara are likely to lose their effectiveness after three to four months. Therefore, it is wise to replace mascara every few months even if it is not completely used up. In the meantime, keep the container tightly closed. Also, in the interest of protecting the sensitive region of the eyes, always apply mascara with extra care. If the hand slips and the wand scratches the cornea, an infection or ulceration may result.

Eye Shadow

See: EYE MAKEUP

Face

Facial Structure. The complex structure of the face is the result of the combined effects of surface features, the skin, the tissue below, and the skull. The face is composed of approximately thirty-nine curves, including the eyebrows, the eyes, and the cheekbones. The fourteen bones and thirty-two teeth which form the skull are covered by over one hundred muscles. The face is an exceedingly pliant region of the human body. The intricate muscular structure below the surface of the skin accounts for the expressiveness of the face.

The skull of man's primate ancestors was dramatically different from our own. The forehead was very narrow and flat, and the jaw was much larger. As the angles of the face steepened over time, the chin developed. The face as a whole remains mankind's most varied as well as variable attribute.

Traditionally, in the developed countries of the West, the ideal shape of the face was thought to be the oval, and elaborate means for creating the illusion of this shape with makeup and hairstyle were devised by beauticians. Very few people actually have an oval face. There are at least six other different shapes: 1) pear-shaped faces have a narrow forehead and a wider chin and jaw; 2) diamond-shaped faces are narrow at the forehead and chin and wide across the cheekbones; 3) round faces have a circular curve at the hairline and chin; 4) square faces are straight across the forehead and jaw; 5) heart-shaped faces have a wide forehead and a narrow chin; and 6) long faces are formed by hollow cheeks and a long, narrow shape. Fortunately, today's trend is to heighten the differences in facial shape, especially those that result from a distinct racial or ethnic inheritance. This trend is reflected in film, television, and advertising where more models and actors are getting work due to the individuality of their faces as opposed to how closely they correspond to a formulaic notion of beauty. However, if desired, extremely pronounced angles or roundness can easily be softened by contouring with foundation, concealer, and blush.

Gender Differences. Some differences in facial structure among humans can be categorized along the lines of gender, race, and age. The differences between the faces of men and women are the most subtle. The female face has fewer muscles and slightly more fatty tissue; this accounts for the smoother skin of most women (especially those in their teens and twenties) as well as the still quality associated with the female face. On average, the face of a woman is four-fifths the size of a man's, and most of her features tend to be smaller. The nose is proportionally smaller, wider, and more concave; the mouth, particularly the upper lip, is smaller; the jaw and brow ridge are less pronounced. In women, eyes are larger, more susceptible to developing shadows both on the lids and below the eyes, and the lashes are longer and stronger in youth. Women's brows grow thinner with age, while a man's grow thicker.

Differences in the face along racial lines, although seemingly the most obvious, are difficult to define and subject to much controversy. Because skin color varies widely even within a given race, many researchers believe racial classifications should be made based on the proportion and shape of the face or variations in hair type.

Aging. Differences in facial structure occur with age. As the years pass, the fatty tissue in the skin which supports and smooths the curves of the face begins to break down, pulling the skin downward and creating a more angular effect. Ultimately, this means a loss of mobility in the face but, at the same time, the face acquires more built-in facial "character."

Personality. Constructing an index of "perfect" individual facial features is an impossible task. Physiognomy, the antiquated study of the meaning of individual facial features, attempts—and fails—to do just that. Overall, beauty is the sum of the parts, not an accounting of the parts themselves. It is the interrelationship among facial features as well as the subtlety of the asymmetry that makes the specialness of a face. Specific detail is completely secondary to the general configuration. All faces are somewhat asymmetrical, or slightly imbalanced. Some faces are beautiful to an individual because they are familiar or because of the associations they stimulate. Associations are informed by emotion. Every experience in a human being's life is colored more or less by emotion. Our notions of beauty are particularly influenced by our emotions. This is why beauty is an elusive topic of discussion. But because the basic human emotions are innate and shared by all but the physically ill, they can often be read on the face, especially with the knowledge of the physical context which elicits them. Infants learn remarkably early how to distinguish between happy, sad, and angry faces. The face is the most trustworthy means of forming initial impressions of both mood and personality. Hippocrates, the father of medicine, believed that the face was the best tool for diagnosing ailments. In any case, whether one is looking for clues about character or health, superficial judgments should be avoided.

Face and Culture. Humans are obsessed with other humans, and thus with human faces. People see faces in dreams, clouds, fires, rocks, the moon. Faces occupy a considerable amount of storage space in the brain as each person learns and remembers an average of ten thousand faces in a lifetime. Artists from civilized and traditional cultures, as well as psychologists, have suggested that the face echoes the appearance of the entire torso, or even that facial features are reminiscent of genitalia. However, it would be very difficult to maintain that the face is the object of so much fascination and preoccupation only because it suggests other, more obviously erotic regions of the body. Anthropologists have found that even among primitive tribes who live together in nakedness, the face remains a central, even sacred, focus of attention. For the Trobrianders of the western Pacific, the face has such deep religious significance as the container of the soul that after a cherished family member dies, his or her skull is preserved and kept near the deceased's spouse at all times.

The notion that the face is the covering of the soul explains why masks are so crucial in the religious rituals of cultures throughout the world. Masks reflect an attempt to capture and expand upon the great emotive capacity of the human face, just as cosmetics do. The origins of both masks and cosmetics are associated with ritual events, ceremonies designed to preserve life, cure sickness, and glorify the gods.

Human beings across the globe and throughout history have acted upon the desire to change the appearance of the face. At its roots, this universal desire is invariably connected with mystical ritualistic practices. Even in today's extremely secular society, the application of cosmetics involves making sacrifices and employing a careful method, both of which are also elements of ceremonial ritual. Women and men engage religiously in the use of powders, perfumes, paints, shadows, highlighters, concealers, liners, etc. in the pursuit of a more engaging face. These routines and the attitudes toward the face they express are intricately involved with the human thirst for self-improvement and the need for a celebratory mask with which to greet the world. All the attention paid this relatively small area of the human body reenforces a claim such as that made by Walt Whitman: "In the faces of men and women I see God" ("Song of Myself").

See also: PHYSIOGNOMY

How to Contour the Face

When applying cosmetics designed to sculpt the contours of the face, it is important to set the stage properly; use overhead, as opposed to eye-level, lighting. Inadequate lighting washes out or obscures the lines of the face, making it impossible to have an accurate perception of the object of scrutiny. Subtly adjusting the natural lines of the face requires knowledge of a few basic principles of shadowing, the relationship between light and dark, and the nature of color. For example, the red tone in blush accentuates the area to which it is applied and rounds the curves of the face. Lighter shades project the regions to which they are applied outward because light, in turn, reflects light. Darker shades absorb light and give the illusion of deeper recession.

Face-lift Surgery (Rhitidectomy)

The face-lift is the second most commonly requested form of cosmetic surgery. (The most frequently performed is rhinoplasty, or nose surgery.) Surgeons perform operations to remove forehead worry lines, eliminate crow's feet, remove bags under the eyes, lift the eyebrows, and smooth wrinkles that form around the mouth. The procedure is relatively, but not completely, painless and requires wearing face bandages for approximately five days after the surgery is performed. The operation involves the removal of skin from certain areas so that the remaining skin is tightened and smoothed against the facial bones. The procedure can be repeated and, contrary to common belief, the tendency to sag is not

Before and after face-lift surgery. The drawing shows where the incision is made and how the skin is pulled up.

increased as a result. Even though it is a fairly common procedure, it does require great delicacy. A surgeon should be chosen with special care. In Paris and a few other major cities, clinics have opened which offer miniface-lifts performed in-house. These are less effective than major surgery and should be considered with even greater caution. Before considering any form of plastic surgery, consider the possibility of corrective makeup first.

A curious footnote: In the eighteenth century, Marechal de Richelieu used homemade daily face-lifts well into his eighties in hopes of continuing his libertine life-style. His servant would stretch the skin of his forehead and cheeks and then secure the folds to a pad that attached to his hair.

See also: COSMETIC SURGERY

Face Powder

Face powder is among the oldest cosmetics. Facial powders were originally designed to create the illusion of noticeably white, flawless skin. The history of cosmetics is filled with peculiar recipes for this basic beauty aid. Ancient Egyptians used crushed marble and powdered chalk to make their face powder. As late as the early twentieth century, American housewives would fill a sock with cornstarch and carry it with them through the day, occasionally buffing it against the nose. Some early face powders were made from crushed eggshells mixed with perfume. Unfortunately, a number of unscrupulous entrepreneurs took advantage of the feminine interest in face powders, and products were made that contained arsenic and other lethal substances until the Food, Drug, and Cosmetic Act of 1938 created concrete industry guidelines for the first time in the United States. In 1866, Henry Tetlow, an American, created the first inexpensive and mass-producible powder base from oxide of zinc.

Today, the manufacture of face powders has become exceedingly refined, both in terms of ingredients used and the range of color and texture available. Its cosmetic function is no longer to attract attention, but to deflect it. Face powder is now used as a filter to blend harsh edges and create an appearance of overall softness and continuity.

Color should be chosen to best complement the wearer's skin tone, allowing her natural complexion to breathe through. Some cosmetologists suggest mixing various shades to achieve the most perfect match possible. If wearing cosmetic foundation, match the shade of the powder carefully to this base.

Powder may be applied exclusively to certain regions of the face that tend toward shininess or as a muting surface to the entire face and neck. It is best to apply powder generously and then remove excess immediately with a brush or absorbent cotton. Powder will also help set makeup on the face as it is somewhat water resistant.

See also: COSMETICS, FOOD AND DRUG ADMINISTRATION (FDA)

Facial Hair

In some Mediterranean and eastern countries women are admired for a downy line on the upper lip. However, most Americans consider facial hair to be a blemish on women—but a sign of maturity, wisdom, and virility on men. The male beard has been a significant symbol in both Western and Middle Eastern mythology. In fact, Queen Hatshepsut, the obelisk builder of ancient Egypt, wore false beards as a symbol of authority.

Several processes for removing unwanted hair are readily available. A process called electrolysis destroys the papillae at the base of the hair follicle, cutting off the supply of blood so that hair can no longer grow. This process involves the use of an electric needle and is somewhat time consuming, but it is the most efficient and reliable means for permanent removal. Diathermy is a bleaching process which gradually weakens the hair. Professional and hot wax treatments are available in salons and can be purchased at most drug stores. Cream bleaches, mixed with activators, are inexpensive and easy to apply at home. It is important to note that tweezing, shaving, and the use of depilatories stimulate future hair growth elsewhere on the face and, therefore, are only semi-permanent measures.

See also: DEPILATORY, ELECTROLYSIS

Facials

Many centuries ago when it was discovered that mud and clay possessed inherent healing properties, the first facial masks were made. These natural substances softened and smoothed the skin and sped the healing of blemishes and wounds. During the reign of Elizabeth I of England (1558–1603), facial masks were very popular. Their ingredients included alum, borax, powdered eggshells, ground almonds, and poppy seeds.

Today, preparations made of both natural and synthetic substances are marketed as facial masks. They come in powder, paste, or gel form. A mask is most effective when applied as the culmination of a full facial treatment, but commercially prepared masks are usually more cost and time effective. Different types of masks are available to fulfill specific tasks such as deep cleansing, toning, exfoliation, moisturizing, or the stimulation of circulation. Some salons offer custom-designed masks made with completely organic ingredients such as bananas, strawberries, avocados, egg whites, yogurt, mayonnaise, glycerine, and herbal teas.

Facials soften and soothe the skin. Given once a week, they work to unclog the pores and stimulate circulation. Application of a facial mask should be preceded by a massage, beginning at the chest, working the fingers in a circular motion progressing upward to the shoulders, neck, and face, toward the scalp.

Facial mask application should always begin on a freshly washed face. Masks are applied to the moist skin where they dry, producing a stimulating, tightening sensation. The moisture generated by the skin through perspiration is retained and reabsorbed into the skin. As long as the face is thoroughly cleaned before the mask is applied, this is quite beneficial for revitalizing dry skin. When the mask is removed, impurities such as dead skin cells and blackheads are removed as well.

See also: MUD, EGG

How to Make a Homemade Face Mask

The following ingredients for homemade facials are suggested (look for the same natural ingredients in commercial facial masks).

- For normal skin—mix oatmeal in warm water; scrub gently into the skin; dry; and then rinse with warm water.

- For dry or sensitive skin—dissolve yeast in warm, distilled water with a few drops of wheat-germ oil; massage into the skin; leave on for ten minutes after it has dried; then rinse with cold water.

- For oily skin—apply one half cup of honey or buttermilk as a thin mask; allow twenty minutes to dry; then rinse with cold water.

False Teeth

See: TEETH

Fashion

Fashion generally refers to a form of behavior that is widely accepted in a society at a certain time. Most notably, "fashion" refers to clothing and accessories that constitute a conventionalized "costume." Fashion becomes an issue the minute wearing clothes becomes something more than a necessity. Interestingly, the idea that clothing can be more than protection from the environment is about as old as human beings themselves.

Fashions always have a limited life span. Because by definition they are about exploring variations, they must change. When a clothing trend lasts a very short time it is more appropriately termed a fad. However, some fashions do persist for an extended period to become what are known as customs or traditions.

Fashion, in a sense, can be seen as the quest for tradition. It is never quite predictable what particular variation in dress will have genuine staying power. In Europe in the early nineteenth century, long pants were introduced as a fashion staple for men, and they later became the dominant style in most countries, still prevalent today. But in another sense, everything has changed! Most significantly, long pants are now a basic component of women's and children's attire as well. And the meaning of "pants" or "trousers" is now defined by an overwhelming number of variables—different fabrics, colors, cuts—and these expand each year.

Technological developments have always influenced the change in styles, in terms of economic and creative possibilities. New dyes led to new color combinations. New fibers, such as nylon, made it possible to introduce new garments such as affordable stockings. The highly automated, industrial mass production of clothes made a wide and fast distribution of new styles possible and enhanced their impact on society.

Today, people mostly follow fashion to be accepted by others and to make themselves attractive according to the changing standards of beauty. The way one dresses makes a strong statement about who one is—his or her social status, personality, or even political beliefs as with the outrageous, free-flowing, uninhibiting apparel of the sixties or the simple, severe, blue uniform of Chinese workers during the Cultural Revolution. Sometimes we think of fashion and uniforms as being completely opposite—uniforms proclaiming that one already belongs to an established group and fashionable dressing indicating that one is out in front dancing to a slightly different drum. But both exist within the same spectrum. Whether we like it or not, our clothes communicate a great deal about who we are, or at least how we would like to be seen.

Historically, fashions often resulted from legally imposed restrictions and obligations that confirmed existing social systems, protected domestic production, or established memberships of certain guilds. In the seventeenth century, for example, men in England were forced by law to wear woolen caps made in England. But this law did not apply to members of the upper class who were permitted to wear hats imported from France and Italy.

Prehistory. Clothes were "discovered" in prehistoric times as a means of protection against the environment. We can only guess what the earliest clothing looked like, but mural paintings in Spain show garments that resemble those of the modern Eskimo. Researchers believe that from the very beginning male and female dress were differentiated. Some evidence indicates that, as early as the fourteenth century, the fundamental elements of European clothing were established.

Ancient Egypt, Greece, and Rome. The Egyptians mainly used linen in their garments. White—the color of linen bleached in the sun—was the color most often used because they had not really mastered the techniques required to dye linen more or less permanently.

The most important garment for men was a kilt—a piece of cloth wrapped around the waist. The length of the cloth and the method used to hold it in place were indicative of social position. Women often went nude, especially in the privacy of their homes. On some occasions, they wore a tight linen skirt held up by suspenders. Both men and women wore wigs and face paint as protection against the harsh sun.

The main article of Greek attire was a long linen or wool shirt, worn over a girdle (a tightly bound undergarment designed to flatten the middle). Length and draping were different for men and women, and also for artisans, soldiers, and slaves. A large, rectangular piece of cloth was used as a mantle.

The Roman mantle or toga was originally worn by men and women of all classes. During the course of history, however, the toga became exclusively a state dress, worn by the emperor and other high officials. A system of colored borders indicated the rank and the function of the officials. Gradually, the toga became so complicated that certain slaves were specially designated to assist with handling the garment. They were the first dressers.

Middle Ages to the Eighteenth Century. The crusaders returning from the Middle East in the twelfth and thirteenth centuries brought back many new styles and fabrics that were previously not available in Europe. From the fourteenth century on, European monarchs started to dictate fashions to the members of their courts. In doing so, they established a highly visible symbol of loyalty. Soon enough, this led to absurd extremes. The nobility would try to outdo one another imitating whatever the king or queen could come up with. Louis XIII of France, who wore a wig to hide his baldness, was promptly copied by scores of Frenchmen who began to shave their heads and put on wigs.

Nineteenth Century to Present. The advent of the industrialized society in the nineteenth century made fashion accessible to more and more people. Fashion no longer expressed a rigid class system, but actually broke down the barrier between classes. Today, it has even led to a breakdown in national barriers. For example, American blue jeans, a symbol of Western freedom and material success, are now coveted by Europeans, Japanese, Russians, and many Middle Easterners alike.

The basic standards of dress in our era, which still allow for significant differences, provide a generally accepted and accessible background against which people can portray their individuality and personality with cosmetics, accessories, and jewelry. The uniformity, in other words, by no means implies identity. Everyone is looking for some common ground with other people. At the same time, we use clothing to express our individual sensory, political, moral, and aesthetic taste. Ironically, the most outrageous innovations in dress, which are born of a desire to change or at least express discontent with the status quo (such as the punk movement of the seventies), frequently trickle down, mellow, and become part of what is extensively acceptable. Now, spiked haircuts, leather jackets, and multiple earrings on men and women are not perceived to be as exorbitantly aggressive or bizarre as they once were. But in general, a marriage between harmony within the culture and radical innovation is the real key to making a meaningful fashion statement.

See also: COSMETICS, JEWELRY

Feet

> "A pretty foot is a great gift of nature."
> —Goethe

> "When my feet hurt, I can't think."
> —Abraham Lincoln

The feet are composed of several joints, muscles, ligaments, and a mere twenty-six bones, including some of the smallest in the body. It is a remarkable engineering achievement that such relatively small structures can support the weight of the entire human body. Each step brings the body's full weight to bear on the foot for an estimated 70,000 miles, or about three trips around the world, during an average lifetime. In spite of the burden that feet are required to bear, civilized societies have introduced a number of means for abusing the feet even while developing methods for their proper care.

The image of an Oriental woman's bound foot, limp and malformed from an excruciating process of slowly crushing the bones over the course of a lifetime, should suggest the importance of avoiding shoes that are too tight. In a world free from such fetishistic practices, a beautiful foot is also a healthy one. Corns and calluses are the most common result of ill-fitting shoes and, although they can be easily cured, they cause a great deal of discomfort and look unattractive. But the misery produced by a pained foot does not stop at the ankle; it invariably manifests itself on the face, in the muscles of the back, and in headaches.

Foot Care. The ancient practice of bathing the feet of royalty is more than ceremonial. It is the mark of intelligent reverence for an overworked and oft-neglected region of the human body. Happily, ninety-eight out of every one hundred Americans are born with normal feet. But by the age of two, twenty-five out of one hundred have developed some defect. And eighty out of one hundred adults experience some form of foot disorder. Aching feet, along with the common cold and headaches, are the most often reported health complaint. The good news is that, royalty or no, almost all foot ailments are reversible with remedial treatment.

Up to 90 to 95 percent of all foot trouble is self-induced. At least 20 percent of American men and 45 percent of American women admit to wearing uncomfortable shoes because they perceive them as being attractive. Aside from ill-fitting shoes, the feet suffer from other forms of neglect. Shoes made from synthetic materials do not allow perspiration to evaporate. Another common problem is overlong toenails. Toenails and cuticles should be examined and trimmed once a week. To avoid ingrown toenails, always cut the nails straight across, not in a curve. When performing a pedicure, avoid scratching the cuticle area, since this makes it vulnerable to infection; soften the cuticle with a cuticle cream before removal. Persons with occupations which entail moving on the feet all day should change their shoes every six hours, avoid especially high heels, and purchase shoes with sturdy arch supports.

The following are a few recommendations for further attending to the needs of the body's foundation:

- Purchase shoes that have plenty of room for the toes, flexible soles, and leather uppers.

- Change socks or stockings at least once a day.

- Soak tired feet in extremely hot or cold baths, which stimulate circulation; the feet also benefit from soakings in Epsom salts solutions.

- Treat calluses with a commercial softening medication. Vigorous application of a pumice stone (a porous, lightweight, volcanic stone) to the sole of the foot softens this especially rough region of the body.

- Apply foot powder to the feet as a preventive against fungus infections after bathing and before donning closed shoes or boots.

- Strengthen and tone the feet by walking barefoot over sand or over a hard, smooth surface.

- Examine the feet regularly for corns. If detected at an early stage, corns can be eliminated before they cause pain. They first appear as a small, hardening circle of skin. Massage the area with lanolin and protect it from further friction with corn pads. Stop wearing the shoes which caused them. A matured corn should be removed surgically.

- Never hone corns or calluses with rough files or razor blades or probe with a sharp instrument. One risks perforating them and making them vulnerable to infection.

Film

Film is the most familiar and accessible art form in contemporary society. Very little time elapsed before film had attained this dominant position in our culture. The technology emerged in the late nineteenth century and, by the nineteen twenties, moviegoing was a crucial part of every American's life. Even during the Great Depression, people flocked to the movie houses in unprecedented numbers every week and paid that hard-earned quarter to see the latest Hollywood release. But film has done more than satisfy essential needs for entertainment and information. Due to the seductive quality of film and its capacity for widespread and immediate dissemination, the movies have had profound effects on the way we perceive ourselves and have influenced our ideals of beauty.

The influence of film is most apparent in the realm of fashion.

Celluloid images have dictated fads in everything from hairstyles to makeup to clothing to body type. The style of a charismatic star is more likely to change the look of the nation than the most powerful ad campaign. Clara Bow, the silent film star of the nineteen twenties, sent many women running to the beauty shop to bob their hair and to the mirror to sculpt their lips into little bows. In the twenties and early thirties, many perceived the incarnation of feminine mystery in the melancholy persona of Greta Garbo, one among the many figures who furthered the cult of the alluring blonde which includes Jean Harlow, Betty Grable, Grace Kelly, Marilyn Monroe, and recent additions such as Meryl Streep, Michele Pfeiffer, and Madonna. Clark Gable inspired many men to grow pencil-thin mustaches and strengthen the muscles controlling their eyebrows. The Joan Crawford look of the nineteen forties—huge padded shoulders, full, blood-red lips, and severe eyebrows—dictated fashions during wartime. A trench coat and scruffy beard became symbols of masculinity and a debonair, dashing life-style thanks to Humphrey Bogart and *Casablanca*. Some other notable examples of styles spread to the culture through film include: the gamine pixie haircut of Audrey Hepburn in *Sabrina*, Jane Russell's full figure (which brought back the popularity of feminine voluptuousness), the cat-eye makeup of Elizabeth Taylor in *Cleopatra*, and the James Dean *Rebel Without a Cause* look—slicked-back hair, faded jeans, T-shirt with not-so-carefully concealed cigarettes, and leather jacket. The visual impressions left by these larger-than-life figures of the screen deeply affected definitions of physical beauty at the time.

Occasionally, the physical traits of certain Hollywood stars even become immortalized as ideals within our language, e.g., "Bette Davis eyes" and "Ann Miller legs." Certainly, almost everyone would understand that if a woman is referred to as a "real Marilyn Monroe" or a man as a "Paul Newman type" the speaker means to say that she or he possesses a smoldering sexuality and a riveting presence.

Aside from the impact of a single star, a blockbuster film with a powerful message or narrative can, in and of itself, form the standard of beauty embraced by the general public. A good place to turn for clues to next year's fashion trends is the present year's nominees for the Best Picture Academy Award. The capacity of film to guide our aesthetic imaginations has only been augmented by the proliferation of moving images in society through television and videos. As visual literacy increases in sophistication, film is bound to continue to shape, in abundantly creative ways, humankind's pursuit of an alluring physical beauty.

Food and Drug Administration (FDA)

The Food and Drug Administration is an agency of the United States federal government within the Department of Health and Human Services. The agency maintains offices and laboratories in over one hundred cities across the United States. One of the FDA's crucial responsibilities is to monitor activity in the cosmetic industry to ensure that products are being marketed fairly and that ingredients are sufficiently healthful and do what the manufacturers claim. As of 1975, manufacturers have been required to list clearly and honestly on a product's package all ingredients contained therein.

Unscrupulous manufacturers were at one time using such lethal substances as arsenic and lead in cosmetics. In reaction to this, Congress passed the Federal Food, Drug, and Cosmetic Act in 1938 to oversee the safe manufacture of products entering the market. This act defines cosmetics as "articles intended to be rubbed, poured, sprinkled, or sprayed on, introduced into, or otherwise applied to the human body or any part thereof for cleansing, beautifying, promoting attractiveness, or altering the appearance." Along with the Drug Amendments Act of 1962, it provides the chief focus for the agency's work.

Foundation

The face-covering, flesh-colored makeup base known as foundation is a relatively new cosmetic invention. The first modern beige foundation, "Mutation Mink," was introduced by Gala in the late 1950s. This innovation was an indication of a major shift away from the ancient Western ideal of a white-and-pink complexion. Chiefly, this change occurred due to the gradual realization that each skin type can be attractive in its own right and most faces are better served by respecting natural coloring than by attempting to dramatically alter it.

Foundations are designed to give the skin a uniform color and to provide a smooth surface for the application of other cosmetics. Foundation should be just slightly darker than one's natural complexion in order to work effectively. Before purchasing a product, test the color by applying a thin layer to a small region on the back of the hand; if the color blends easily so as to be virtually imperceptible, a match has been found. The range of human skin color is extremely broad; there are over forty shades of black skin alone. However, the range of foundation shades produced by cosmetic manufacturers today has a palette that can almost rival the one found in nature.

See also: CONCEALERS, COSMETICS

How to Apply Foundation

- Dab a small amount of foundation on the throat, the chin, the bridge of the nose, the forehead, and the most prominent point of each cheekbone.
- Disperse evenly with a small facial makeup sponge.
- Blend makeup so that no obvious line is visible below the chin or on the neck.
- Dust the face with loose powder in a coordinated shade.

France

> *"Il n'y a pas de femme laide!"*
> ("There is no such thing as a plain woman.")
> —French proverb

> *"We don't feel at ease here: we are surrounded by too much beauty."*
> —Colette, a comment on her fellow Parisians

For centuries, France has been the beauty capital of the world. The French have contributed more to the art of cultivating personal beauty than any other culture. During the reign of Louis XIV, women were said to have spent as much as twelve hours in preparation for a ball. At times, the imaginative contributions that come out of France seem quite outrageous. In the eighteenth century, a practice was invented called *les mouches*, decorating the face with tiny black stars and crescents made of velvet or paper to conceal the unpleasant facial scars left by the ravishes of smallpox. Cartouches, or love patches, were similar inventions. These patches were used as social codes as well as to hide blemishes.

The French are unequaled at culling the beauty secrets from older Eastern cultures, refining them through scientific procedures, and then disseminating them to the Western world. These secrets include the manufacture of perfume, henna, and facial masks, as well as the arts of aromatherapy and wig making. Some of the other unique contributions of the French to beauty culture include high heels (from the seventeenth century), hydrotherapy, lipstick in a cartridge (1910), and the face-lift (both temporary and surgical).

In the fourteenth century, long before the advent of fashion magazines, designers would send dolls from Paris to the various courts of Europe to disseminate the latest fashions. This practice was still in play in the nineteenth century as a means for sending the latest styles across the Atlantic to America.

In fact, "France" and "fashion" seem intertwined in most people's imaginations. The vast majority of designers have come out of or settled in France. The annual tradition of looking to Paris for indications of next year's trends and the newest innovations is deeply entrenched. As a source of inspiration, many artists and designers have claimed that Paris in particular is inexhaustible.

Just as with their passion for fine food and wine, a pride and respect for their artists pervades the entire French culture. Just as film stars in the United States influence beauty ideals today, the French have always used the influences of contemporary novelists and painters in creating prescriptions for beauty. From George Sand's athletic heroines in the mid nineteenth century to the black-clothed, smoke-enshrouded café crowd associated with the existentialists before and during World War II, designers have turned to more intellectual aesthetes for inspiration. The relationship between high culture and personal beauty accounts, to a large extent, for the rich offerings France has continuously provided.

Freckles

Freckles are the concentration of melanin (the pigment that allows people to tan) in a single spot on the skin. The word "freckles" is derived from a Scandinavian word meaning "to sprinkle." Freckles are generally caused by the sun, but in some cases, they can even be caused by long-term exposure to strong electric light. The tendency to develop freckles is hereditary. Fair-complexioned persons are much more likely to acquire freckles, but if desired they may be minimized by avoiding the sun and using sun blocks. Despite the claims of some cosmetic folklore, freckles cannot be removed with sour cream, cucumber juice, or lemon juice, although the latter can mute them with its bleaching action. One old folk remedy for freckles was the application of sublimate of mercury. However, this substance not only removed freckles but also the skin and even the flesh below!

Today in the West a uniform, lily-white complexion is no longer the pinnacle of feminine beauty. Many people now regard freckles as an asset rather than a blemish. Quite a few movie stars and fashion models proudly display a freckled face that in former days would have been erased by the photographer's airbrush.

How to Lighten Freckles

If freckles genuinely make one uncomfortable, skin bleaching creams are available in pharmacies that safely lighten freckles. Avoid products which contain mercury salts or bismuth; they dry the skin and cause wrinkles. Other more drastic (and comprehensive) methods for freckle removal require professional supervision. First consult a dermatologist for advice.

Freckles can be temporarily lightened with a mask of 1/4 cup buttermilk, 1/2 teaspoon horseradish, and 1 tablespoon oatmeal (ground). Mix ingredients into a paste, apply to the freckled areas (except around the eyes); and leave for thirty minutes.

Freshener

See: ASTRINGENT

Glasses

"Men seldom make passes at girls who wear glasses."
—Dorothy Parker

The above quotation, although a clever poetic line, could hardly be considered an accurate assessment in this day and age. More than half of the women in America wear glasses. Glasses, both corrective and sunglasses, are now perceived as a valuable fashion accessory. Extensive designer lines are available to complement all face shapes, life-styles, and fashion statements. Makeup experts generally recommend choosing frames that contrast with the shape of one's face. For example, a person with an angular face should wear glasses with curved frames. The eyebrows should be covered by the frame so that the appearance of the chin is not weakened. To make the nose look smaller, choose glasses with a low bridge. If the bridge piece is straight and clear, the eyes will seem wider apart. The color of a frame should be chosen to either complement or blend with hair, eye, and skin coloring. Before settling on frames, inspection in a three-sided mirror will reveal the appearance of the eyewear from all angles.

Women who wear glasses can afford to wear slightly more defined eye makeup. Always remember to check the application after returning glasses to the face! Those who wear contact lenses can also alter or brighten their eye color at the same time with special colored lenses.

Greece

Greek philosophers such as Plato and Aristotle were very concerned with the nature of beauty. They believed that beauty involved symmetry, harmony, radiance, balance, and the divine. The Greeks desired stature and balanced proportions in art and architecture as well as in the faces and forms of their "beautiful" people. This ideal of beauty was spread by their coinage, coins being regarded as miniature works of sculpture.

On a more concrete level, the ancient Greeks pursued beauty through the use of cosmetics. The Greeks used perfumes and cosmetics lavishly in religious rites, for pleasure, and for medicinal purposes. The women who used cosmetics were almost exclusively courtesans. (Greek men also used cosmetics!) This was the first time in history when a demarcation between ordinary women and prostitutes could be made in terms of the quantity of cosmetics used. Courtesans used face powder made from white lead; lined their eyes with kohl; dyed the hair with yellow flower petals and potassium solutions; and put vermillion, a bright red pigment made from ground cinnabar, on their cheeks and lips. On the other hand, there was no stigma attached to being a "painted women"; courtesans actually had a more respected position in Greek society than other women.

H

Hair

In mammals, the chief biological purpose of hair is to provide warmth, but in humans, hair has always been perceived as a cosmetic feature. Hair forms a border for the face, like a frame around a portrait, that can either accentuate or detract from the beauty of the face. This is why cosmetologists stress the significance of choosing hair products and styles carefully. A human head of hair is comprised of approximately 100,000 strands that demand proper attention.

Technically speaking, hairs are actually flexible, slender skin structures. The presence of hair (or fur) on an organism is one means of identifying it as a mammal. Hair is dead, insoluble protein, mostly keratin, which is also the principal component of nails, horns, and hoofs. The hair shaft—the name given to each individual strand after it has traveled about one third of the way from the root to the skin surface—is composed of three layers of dead cells. 1) The medulla, located at the center, appears to transport gases and nutrients to the rest of the hair and may provide one explanation for how day-to-day fluctuations in the appearance of the hair are possible. 2) The cortex contains the pigment that determines hair color. 3) The cuticle protects against excessive evaporation. The only "living" aspect of hair is a few growing cells located at the follicle.

Hair follicles are the baglike structures below the surface of the skin that contain the hair bulb. The hair bulb is where cells divide, resulting in hair growth. The blood that enables cell growth is supplied by way of the papilla which projects into the hair bulb at the base of the follicle and contains a capillary. As the divided cells push their way upward, they are no longer supplied with the nutrients necessary to sustain life. At this point, keratinization, or the transformation of the cells into protein structures, occurs. This process is completed long before the hair actually emerges from the surface of the skin.

Hair growth occurs cyclically. Human hair follicles are active continuously for two to six years, followed by a three-month rest period. These phases are, of course, out of synchronization; only 5 to 15 percent of the hairs in the scalp are resting at one time. Growth per month is generally about half an inch. Hair follicles are actually the most productive metabolizers in the human body. The speed with which hair grows is affected by diet, age, sex, weather (hair tends to grow more rapidly in summer), and general health. As a matter of fact, dull-looking hair is often one of the first indications of illness. This is somewhat mysterious, since hair is technically dead.

Hair receives lubrication from the oil produced by sebaceous glands in the skin. This oil accounts for the hair's soft texture. The extent of softness is also a function of the shape of the hair cells; paradoxically, curly hair cells are very flat, while straight hair cells are round. The round cells of straight hair give it a softer texture; the flat cells producing curly hair give it a sharper, more bristlelike feeling.

The natural color of hair is mostly determined by the distribution of melanin, a brown-black pigment. Light-colored hair, including gray and white shades, is the result of the absence of pigment. There is also a relationship between color and the fullness of the hair. Blondes tend to have more hair than anyone else, approximately 150,000 hairs; but light hair also tends to be finer. The average number of hairs varies with color, from brown (115,000), black (110,000) to red (90,000). But full-

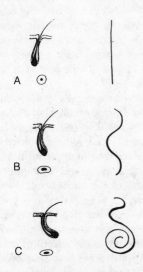

Different shapes of hair:
A. Straight B. Wavy C. Curly

ness is also determined by the thickness of individual hair shafts. The diameter of hair shafts can be augmented with protein shampoos, body-building conditioners, and coloring products that permanently swell the hair shaft.

Many factors influence the way hair looks, and to a large extent they are genetic. But a change in diet can dramatically improve the hair's appearance. Adequate minerals and vitamins are crucial for healthy hair—particularly iron, sulfur, zinc, and the B-complex vitamins. It is important to nurture the body which produces the hair because the hair is one of the most alluring physical attributes.

Hair and Beauty. Literature is sprinkled with references to the seductive quality of human hair. Eighteenth century English poet Alexander Pope wrote in his famous poem "The Rape of the Lock" about the enchantress Lorelei who sat on the banks of the Thames combing her golden hair, the sight of which lured men to their destruction:

> *Fair tresses man's imperial race insnare,*
> *And Beauty draws us with a single hair.*

The hair of Biblical figures such as Samson and Absalom—a son of King David—was a source of physical strength; Samson, a mighty warrior, became helpless when Delilah shaved his head while he slept. In ancient Nordic legends, men were, quite literally, entangled in the hair of Sylvan women which was so delicate as to be indistinguishable from sunlight. These tales echo similar sentiments expressed by many other literary authors such as James Howell: "One hair of a woman can draw more than a hundred pair of oxen."

However, poets have not been the only members of society to acknowledge the power of lustrous hair. Hair makes a perfect feature for symbolism because it is accessible, easily manipulated, cut without pain, and grows quickly enough that all experiments are only temporary. There are thousands of ways to manipulate the hair—dyeing, frizzing, straightening, removing, shaping, and arranging.

Evidence of the pursuit of beautiful, full, healthy hair peppers the annals of history. Assyrians wore elaborately curly hairstyles. As early as 400 B.C. some Grecian women dyed their hair, and this practice was also quite common among the women of ancient Rome. Romans also developed the first primitive curling irons. The first hair lacquer (the antecedent to modern hair spray) was developed in ancient Japan in order to secure the complicated coiffures of aristocratic women. In exploring old European court journals one finds such archaic recipes as the following:

For thickening hair—Take a hare's foot, some date-stroves and the hoof of an ass. Heat these ingredients in oil. Then apply by "friction."

For eliminating gray hairs—Apply the blood of a black calf or black bull or the fat of a black snake to the surface in question.

Historically, the attainment and maintenance of beautiful hair is not solely a feminine preoccupation. Even frontiersmen expanding the boundaries of the continental United States during the nineteenth century were not utterly free from this inclination; borrowing a practice from the Indians, they used bear grease to smooth their hair down in the mornings or in preparation for a rare social gathering.

Hair and History. The hair symbolizes many things in different cultures, and these meanings are never trivial. In early pagan societies, the hair was perceived as a repository for at least part of the soul, which is why a lock of hair was often used as part of magical charms or talismans. An Egyptian widow would bury her husband with a lock of her hair to protect him in the afterlife. In pagan rites of spring, braided hair is a symbol of the interweaving of masculine and feminine powers. In the ancient culture of India, hair represents divine energy. Julius Caesar cut off the hair of the conquered Gauls as a symbol of power; this mark of submission to authority is still worn by criminals and members of the military.

In most cultures, long hair for men has been the rule rather than the exception. French noblemen during the Renaissance began wearing the hair cropped short. At this time, the French court was already acknowledged as the beauty capital of the world, and exhibiting a characteristic Francophile attitude, King Henry VIII of England ordered all Englishmen to do likewise. However, many nobles in both countries continued to wearing long, flowing periwigs. During the course of history, most men have worn short hair only in periods of military rule or during times characterized by frequent military campaigns. The Puritans under Oliver Cromwell took the short haircut for men to an extreme in symbolic rejection of the excesses of the aristocracy. Cromwell's followers were known as Roundheads from the closely trimmed hairstyle they wore.

Other examples of hair being used as a symbol of social rebellion include the long hair of the hippies during the sixties in the United States, the brutally shaved heads of skinhead gangs, the bushy Afro worn as a symbol of Black pride and the outrageous mohawks and spiked looks of the English punk-rockers inaugurated by the Sex Pistols during the nineteen seventies. On the other end of the spectrum, elaborate hairstyles and wigs, through most of history, have been a mark of the elevated social standing that afforded men and women the leisure time to attend to such modes and employ others to do so.

Alteration. Historically, manipulation of the hair has been the concern of many cultures. Hairdressing as a profession has been common only since the eighteenth century, yet archaeologists have unearthed hairpins and ornaments that date back to 8000 B.C. during the New Stone Age. It is interesting to note that in the eighteenth century, wearing the hair down marked a lunatic or a strumpet, while current fashion defines abundant hair, waved and loosely worn, as highly appealing. During the early Renaissance, many women shaved their hairlines in order to emphasize the forehead and emulate the ideals depicted in such paintings as Botticelli's *Simonetta*. The softly puffed, romantic hairstyle of the 1890s was copied from the illustrations created by the American artist Charles Dana Gibson, whose work was seen and admired throughout the United States and Europe.

Hair is the most readily changeable human physical aspect, and changing the hair can alter one's entire appearance most easily. Most beauty consultants recommend choosing a hairstyle in accord with one's features, life-style, and mode of dress as opposed to how attractive the style may appear on a professional model. Fashions in hairstyles experience radical changes, and the modern tendency is to have simple, natural-looking, and manageable hairstyles. But acquiring a new hairstyle remains for many a serious ritual—either invigorating or terrifying. Many hairstylists assume the role of shaman for their clients, acting simultaneously as therapist, magician, and aesthetician. For these services, they often receive impressive financial remuneration, far greater than most artists.

While elaborate wigs, worn for weeks at a time to reduce time-consuming labor, once signified the epitome of elegance, simple coiffures are now the preference of executives and most active members of our fast-paced contemporary society. Although throughout history long hair for women (and, in many instances, men as well) has been the dominant preference, shorter styles have gained ascendency ever since bobbed hair came into fashion in the nineteen twenties.

See also: HAIR DYEING, HAIR MAINTENANCE, HAIR PROBLEMS, PERMANENT

Hair Conditioners

See: CONDITIONERS

Hair Dyeing

A change in hair color is one of the most dramatic ways to transform overall appearance. The effect can be amazing. Many Hollywood stars have experienced a dramatic escalation of their careers merely through a change in their hair color. The practice of hair dyeing dates at least as far back as ancient Egypt. Egyptian men employed the blood of black cows boiled in oil to cover a graying mane. Egyptian women used henna, indigo, sage, and chamomile to change their hair color. Two early Germanic tribes, the Angles and the Saxons (from which we get the racial classification of Anglo-Saxon), reportedly dyed their hair vivid shades of green, blue, and orange. The ancient Gauls, precursors of the French, dyed their hair bright red. After the Civil War, although a dramatic decline occurred in the general use of cosmetics, hair dyeing increased.

Because of the Roman fondness for fair hair, bleaching has a long history. The poet Ovid mentions the fact that the German herb chamomile was sought after for this purpose. In Italy during the High Renaissance, women would apply a recipe of "2 pounds of alum, 6 ounces of black sulphur and 4 ounces of honey" and then sit in the sun for hours in order to bleach their hair blond. In 1880, the "peroxide blonde"

Chamomile

came into vogue in the United States. In 1885, paraphenylenediamine, the chemical base used in most modern tints, was first developed. For many centuries, most hair dyes were used to darken the natural shade of the hair. To achieve a lighter shade, a person had to bleach the hair and then apply a dye. Clairol developed the first one-step hair-coloring product in 1950 called Miss Clairol Hair Color Bath. Today hair coloring products come in six categories:

Rinses add temporary color and are designed to wash out gradually with each shampooing, generally taking from two weeks to several months depending on the strength of the product and the duration of its initial application.

Temporary dyes are designed for minor color alterations. Using them for a radical change in color will likely result in streaking or irregular coverage.

Semipermanent dyes contain no peroxide and are made from a combination of vegetable and chemical substances. They cannot be used to lighten hair but can add shine to one's natural shade or cover graying hair.

Permanent dyes, as the name implies, are designed to grow out with the hair. They are more powerful and can be used to achieve more dramatic changes in shade; they actually alter the cortex at the center of the hair shaft. While permanent dyes last longer, they also require more maintenance to remain attractive. Because most hair grows at a rate of one half inch per month, roots need to be touched up approximately every month or two to avoid a sloppy and blatantly unnatural look.

Bleaches are among the most damaging products that can be applied to the hair. Bleaches are largely comprised of ammonia, which strips the hair of its color, and peroxide (the catalyst). Neither of these chemical substances is healthful. The bleaching process involves an abrasive action against the hair's outer cuticle. For lightening the hair, highlighting is a better option because the chemicals utilized are less potent and they don't come in contact with the scalp. Furthermore, the highlighting process enables the cosmetician to focus on smaller portions of hair scattered throughout, making a more natural look.

Vegetable dyes are nontoxic, natural dyes. They do not alter the structure of hair. Instead, they cling to hair cuticles, coating them and increasing the hair's body. The most common vegetable dye is henna which is made from the ground leaves of the henna plant. The characteristic shades associated with henna are warm, red hues. Vegetable dyes gradually wash out with each shampooing. Other vegetable dyes include chamomile (which lightens) and eggplant (which darkens).

Hair dyes are becoming increasingly sophisticated. Manufacturers developed metallic dyes (marketed as hair or color "restorers"), to counter a dissatisfaction with the range of colors and degree of permanency possible with vegetable dyes. However, hair dyed with these products is more difficult to condition and resists permanent waving. Aniline or oxidation colorants, often in the form of highlighting and tinting shampoos, inject artificial pigment into the hair cortex. These products often make the hair more manageable since the hydrogen peroxide they contain displaces the cuticle just enough to infuse it with some body. Streaking and frosting some strands or regions of the head is another effective means for providing a boast to the appearance of one's hair. Also, touch-ups are required less frequently than with a comprehensive dye treatment.

Today hair coloring can be performed inexpensively and in a manner that improves not only the color but also the texture of the hair. It is estimated that seven out of every ten women dye their hair, and the number of men who do so is steadily increasing. However, any dramatic change in one's hair color should involve professional consultation. Many professionals also recommend a strand test to preview the results a particular dye will produce. This simply means following the steps for the entire procedure but using only a few strands of hair removed from the head in order to determine the duration necessary to achieve the desired shade.

Persons with colored hair should avoid excessively hot water when shampooing, the use of dry shampoos, and too much exposure to the sun, chlorinated water, and salt water. The sun is especially harsh on any head of hair, but processed hair is automatically depleted of moisture so it may easily crack and split. Excessive heat also causes the color to warp.

Some dyes can cause an allergic reaction. The cosmetics industry is becoming more and more knowledgeable in this area every year. A person may use a particular dye for years and then suddenly develop an allergic reaction due to some change in body chemistry. Some municipal and state health boards require a patch test on the skin at the base of the hairline twenty-four hours before a dye is professionally applied in order to detect a possible allergy. If irritation in the form of itching, blisters, or redness occurs another product should be selected.

See also: HAIR, HENNA

Hair Maintenance

"The real sin in life is to abuse and destroy beauty, even one's own— even more, one's own, for that had been put in our care and we are responsible for its well-being."

—Katherine Anne Porter

Beautiful hair is one of the most coveted beauty assets. Articles offering information about the best means for acquiring "fabulous" hair are a regular feature in most fashion and beauty magazines. The focus varies, but the most recurrent themes center around manageability, texture, luster, and style. Due to the laws of genetics, some physical features are more rigidly defined than others. However, the general appearance of the hair can be altered dramatically through maintenance. Because the hair reflects the general health of the entire body, it is important to indulge it with proper care.

The old prescription that a woman should brush her hair one hundred strokes every day actually has some validity. "Exercising" the hair by way of rigorous brushing is effective for making the hair more manageable, although one hundred strokes may be a bit much. The effectiveness of this procedure can be augmented by bending the head forward and brushing from the scalp. Stimulation of the scalp, through massaging and energetic brushing, brings blood to the hair follicles which prompts growth and maintains sheen. However, if the hair has been weakened from overprocessing, it is best to brush the hair gingerly until it has been revitalized through treatment. For long hair, tossing it freely also acts as a stimulant as does gently pulling sections of the hair for several minutes each day. However, the ends of the hair, being furthest from the pores of the skin which generate moisture, are the driest and require more delicate treatment in order to avoid breakage.

The condition of the hair is affected by a number of factors. These include fatigue, stress, or an overly lean or rich diet. Continuous use of hair dyes, highly alkaline shampoos, hair dryers, and heated hair curlers weakens the hair so that it splits and breaks off more easily. However, the most common cause of dull, lackluster hair is a filmy buildup of shampoo due to inadequate rinsing after washing. Soap buildup leaves a residue that attracts dust and germs which compound the problem. Therefore, after shampooing, the hair should be rinsed until rubbing the hands against individual strands produces a squeak. Rinses made with acetic acid are especially effective for eliminating buildup. Hair care products made with natural botanicals—such as chamomile, ginseng, jojoba, henna, and aloe vera—and with amino acids have restorative properties.

Most products are designed to treat three types of hair: dry, normal, and oily. Hair type can be determined by the frequency of shampooing required to sustain a healthy shine under average conditions. (Individuals leading exceptionally physical lives require more frequent washings.) Normal hair requires shampooing once or twice weekly, on the average. Dry hair should be washed once a week, and extremely oily hair may require daily washing. There are two kinds of dry hair: hair which is naturally dry due to fewer oil glands in the scalp, and hair which has become dry as a result of excessive exposure to heat. Each requires a different kind of treatment. Heat-damaged hair has been weakened and will not benefit from hot oil treatments, which can do wonders for naturally dry hair. Heat-damaged hair should be given a protein strengthening treatment, and an alternative grooming routine should be embraced, at least temporarily.

See also: CONDITIONERS, SHAMPOO

Hair Problems

Many serious hair problems are actually problems of the scalp. They may be due to age, stress, or simple negligence. Problem hair can also be a signal of a malady originating elsewhere in the body. If preventive measures of cleanliness and conditioning prove insufficient, or if a change in climate, life-style, etc. triggers major problems, education is the necessary first step toward restoration of the hair's natural beauty.

Dandruff. Dandruff is simply the name for the dead flakes of skin that accumulate on an abnormally dry scalp. Dandruff may be treated with a variety of medically formulated shampoos. However, all shampoos should be used in moderation as extensive shampooing further dries the skin and perpetuates the difficulty. The hair brush must be kept clean, otherwise dandruff can be returned to the scalp with the next brushing. Severe cases of dandruff may be caused by a bacterial infection and require a physician's care. However, dandruff itself is not contagious.

Scalp Disorders. Other scalp disorders include ringworm and head lice. Ringworm is caused by fungi, tiny plants that feed on keratin, the chief component of hair. The fungi causes hair to break off, leaving bare patches of the scalp exposed. Children are especially susceptible to ringworm. It is highly infectious and can be contracted from cats or dogs and spread by way of combs.

Head lice are tiny parasitic insects that secure themselves to the scalp and suck blood. Their eggs are attached to the hair by a gummy substance secreted by the insects. Head lice are also highly contagious. The best preventive is cleanliness. Medically prescribed shampoos, lotions, and creams will aid in their removal.

Losing Hair. For most of a person's life, the hair is continually replacing itself. Therefore, one is always losing hair. Short-term hair loss or thinning can occur after pregnancy and during illness when the growth phase of hair follicles is cut off. Alopecia, or baldness, occurs when hair follicles die and can no longer produce fresh hair growth. Baldness is more marked in men because men are initially endowed with fewer hair follicles per square inch than women. Thus, male hair loss is more easily discernible. Stress, which causes a tightening of the scalp, increases the likelihood of hair loss. Baldness can also be caused or accelerated by scalp infections, radiation, and as a reaction to drugs. Products containing an antibaldness compound, derived from retinol and related to a substance currently used in some antiacne drugs, are expected to enter the United States market soon.

Dryness. Excessive dryness of the hair shaft, resulting in "split ends," (technically termed trichoptilosis), is often caused by long-term application of excessive heat and harsh chemicals to the hair. Extended exposure to chlorine and ultraviolet rays is also potentially damaging. Because hair is continuously replacing itself until the actual follicle dies, these effects can be remedied over time by implementing a conditioning treatment.

Gray Hair. Gray hair, or canities, is the result of a loss of pigment in the hair. Congenital canities appears in albinos, and some people are born with, or quickly develop patches of pigmentless hair. Acquired canities is generally the result of aging. Premature graying can be caused by anxiety, stress, prolonged illnesses, various wasting diseases, and heredity.

See also: BALDNESS, HAIR, HAIR MAINTENANCE, HAIR TRANSPLANT SURGERY, HAIR WEAVING, TOUPEE

Hair Transplant Surgery

Hair transplants involve the removal of hair from one part of the body to another. This process has been practiced since 1959 with excellent results. The procedure is relatively simple and can be performed in the doctor's office under mild sedation. Twenty-five to one hundred hair plugs may be removed and transplanted in one session. The number of sessions required depends on the size of the bald patch to be covered and the amount of follicles available for transplant. The hair which is moved must come from follicles likely to maintain normal production for the remainder of one's life. If transplanting is successfully accomplished, new hair will sprout within three months. A full growth of hair will not appear for ten months.

Hair transplants do work, although not for all men. There must be a healthy fringe of hair on some portion of the head for the procedure to

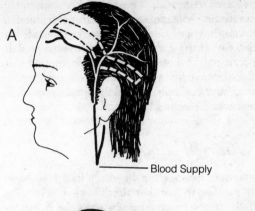

Blood Supply

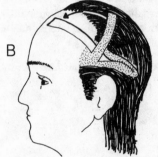

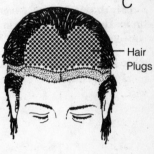

Hair Plugs

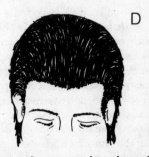

Before and after hair transplantation. The illustration shows a transplant where a flap of skin still bearing hair and containing abundant blood vessels is moved from the side to the front of the head (Figures A and B). The uncovered area is filled with hair plugs (C). Figure D shows the final result.

have much chance of success. Foreheads are particularly resistant to transplants. To rectify a receding hairline, scalp-flap or scalp-reduction surgery—two efficient, safe, but fairly complex surgical methods for transferring hair from one part of the scalp to another—are required. It is important to remember that all of these procedures are costly and that nearly a year passes before the benefits are apparent.

The surgical implant of artificial hair is soundly discouraged. It is highly dangerous—likely to cause serious infections.

Hair Weaving

Hair weaving is a temporary process for disguising hair loss. New, matching human hair is attached to hair that already exists. When the natural hair grows and falls out the process must be repeated. Although initially the least expensive means for concealing hair loss, maintenance can make hair weaving ultimately a far more costly investment than a toupee or hair transplants.

See also: HAIR, HAIR PROBLEMS, HAIR TRANSPLANT SURGERY, TOUPEE

Hands

> *"Hands are the heart's landscape."*
> —Pope John Paul II,
> *Easter Vigil and Other Poems*

Two million years ago, the first genuine human emerged, known as *Homo habilis,* or handy man. Bipedal locomotion, or walking upright on two feet, freed the hands for use in manipulating the objects and materials in man's environment. Fingernails, which are found only in primates, are a specialization that further aids the usefulness of the hands. The hand is indeed a special part of human anatomy. It serves mechanical, creative, and expressive functions. Isaac Newton remarked that the "thumb alone would convince me of the existence of God." Indeed, the shape of the human hand, with its opposable thumb, is a distinguishing characteristic that allows us greater adaptability than most other animals. Interestingly, the development of the hand and an increase in brain size occurred in tandem.

The hand contains at least four types of nerve endings, which accounts for its high sensitivity. The friction ridges covering the skin surface on the palm and fingers increase tactile sensitivity and the ability to grip. The complexity of these ridges and the unique prints each individual's hand will produce as a result has been utilized as a means of identification since at least A.D. 700 in China.

The condition of the hands can indicate disease and aid in diagnosis. The expression "iron hand in a velvet glove," attributed to King Charles V, is an apt definition of the ideal, healthy hand, one which combines strength of grip with softness of skin. Nervous exhaustion can be detected in damp, clammy hands. Transparent skin with exposed veins and a lifeless grip can be indications of poor nutrition, general weakness, or drug abuse. The only "lily-white hands" are the hands of the dead. Large knuckles may be a sign of rheumatism. Trembling hands may indicate Parkinson's disease, alcoholism, or nervousness. X rays of ossification patterns in the hands of children can be used to chart general growth rates.

Hands also play an important role as the instruments of nonverbal expression. Gestures are used not only to augment speech but also to form a language of their own—sign language—which assists in communication in foreign lands, as a substitute for speech for the hearing impaired, or when circumstances prevent oral speech, and as a significant part of the craft of dancers, actors, and public speakers.

Hands and Beauty. Poets, theologians, and artists use the hands as a symbol of union, support, supplication, strength, and control. In the Psalms, Christ used clean hands as a metaphor for spirituality: " . . . who shall stand in this holy place? He that hath clean hands and a pure heart." Expressions that refer to the hands as emblems of feminine control existed even in times when women had very little control outside of the domestic sphere, e.g., "she has him in the palm of her hand" and "he is wrapped around her little finger." The reverential quality of the hands has been captured beautifully in sculptures such as Auguste Rodin's *The Secret* and in other visual art forms like Dürer's drawing *Praying Hands*.

An eighteenth century grand dame reputedly declared that in order for a woman to have beautiful hands her family must have experienced five generations of leisure. With or without the ability to claim such ancestral good fortune, women and many men have gone to great lengths to cultivate soft, delicate-looking hands. American colonials would wear "chicken gloves" to bed at night. These gloves were made of leather treated with crushed almonds and fat from the sperm whale. Sarah Bernhardt dressed her hands with butter. Today, hand lotions are made with many natural and aromatic ingredients such as aloe vera, jojoba, lanolin, rose water, and glycerine.

Care. Hands should be treated with care. They are one of the first parts of the body to show age. When engaging in manual labor, take time to moisturize the hands before and after. To prevent calluses, wear gloves during especially arduous work such as hauling, gardening, and horse-back riding. Whenever possible, wear rubber gloves while doing house-work. Water, cold weather, and overexposure to the sun are also rough on the hands. Protect the hands with a layer of lotion or cream. The acid in lemon juice helps seal in moisture and remove odors from the hands. The hand is a feature unique to human beings and should reflect both the strength and gentleness of which human beings are capable.

Helen of Troy

"Terrible is the likeness of her face to immortal goddesses."
—Homer, *The Iliad*

Beauty was at the heart of the greatest war of ancient mythology, namely, the Trojan War. The war was instigated when three of the most powerful goddesses of the Greek pantheon, Aphrodite, Athena, and Hera, got into an argument over who was the most beautiful. They sought out a young, attractive Trojan prince named Paris to answer the question for them. Each of the goddesses made an attempt to bribe the young man. However, Aphrodite, who promised to bestow on him the most beautiful woman in the world, proved the most persuasive.

The "most beautiful female mortal" was Helen of Troy. She was the daughter of Leda, a mortal, and Zeus, king of the gods. Zeus came to Leda in the form of a swan and seduced the young virgin with his irresistible beauty. As the story is told, Helen was actually hatched from an egg. The powerful repercussions which result from this germination are captured in the poem "Leda and the Swan" by the Irish Modernist poet, W. B. Yeats: "A shudder in the loins engenders there/The broken wall, the burning roof and tower/And Agamemnon dead." Yeats is alluding to the passion-ate expenditure of blood which was to be the legacy of Helen; specifically, it refers to the destruction of the ancient city of Troy resulting from He-len's abduction and the later murder of Agamemnon (Helen's brother-in-law) upon his return home from the war by Helen's sister, his wife, Clytemnestra. These themes in Greek mythology are treated repeatedly in the Greek tragedies and much of Western literature.

Helen's beauty was noted from early childhood onward. Before she reached adolescence, she was kidnapped by the Athenian warrior, The-seus, but was quickly returned to her family. Many suitors vied for her affection, but she eventually married the Spartan king, Menelaus, brother of Agamemnon.

All of this took place before the notorious feud among the goddesses. Thus, the fulfillment of Aphrodite's promise to Paris was no easy task. The goddess was required to enlist her immortal powers in order to assist Paris in abducting Helen. The successful abduction of Helen was the cause of the ten-year-long Trojan War. Poets have treated the elements of this story and particularly Helen's role in the affair in widely divergent fashions. However, the majority perceive her as an innocent victim of her own overwhelming beauty. Although men may curse the human frailty that caused blood to be shed over a pretty face, most, like the Trojan elders in Homer's epic, took one look at Helen and understood. This myth, like history, seems to indicate that men do not go to war because they are hungry or crave power, but in defense of beauty, truth, honor, and the spirit.

See also: APHRODITE

Henna

Henna, or *Lawsonia inermis*, is a plant originally found in the Eastern Hemisphere. It is a member of the loosestrife family, possessing minute red and white flowers and a fragrance similar to roses. The term "henna" is commonly applied to the substance extracted from the leaves of this plant.

The substance works as a natural hair dye, usually producing an auburn tint. However, henna comes in a range of shades from strawberry blond to ebony. It is purchased in powder form, mixed with water, and then applied to the head as a gloppy paste. The henna sets in from fifteen minutes to an hour depending on the shade desired.

Although this method of hair coloring has been employed in the Orient for centuries, henna did not arrive in the United States, via Paris, until 1910. Today, henna is a staple in most beauty salons and can be purchased in a wide variety of shades in many health care and beauty supply stores and even local drugstores. Henna, like chemically manufactured rinses, washes out gradually with each shampooing. Henna is also used in its neutral, or noncolored, form as an ingredient in shampoos and conditioners. It acts as a restorative by coating individual hair strands, thereby strengthening them.

Although henna does not damage hair, it has a couple of drawbacks: 1) it is messy; and 2) because henna leaves a light film on the hair, the dye is not compatible with any form of permanent hair dye or wave.

High Heels

Although the practice of wearing high heeled shoes has been criticized in recent years because of the stress it places on the ankle and lower back, many women persist in wearing them both on the job and out on the town. Why is this so?

High heels were popularized by aristocrats of the seventeenth century French court. These shoes were originally perceived as a remarkable innovation as they kept the wearer's foot relatively free from mud. Also, they were an apt metaphor for the elevated social status of those who wore them. The lift of the heel exaggerated the strut of the stylish and emblematized the sense of confidence that accompanied their wealth—as if they wished their peers to know, "I have no fear of heights!" Of course, cobblestone streets and less than delicate craftsmanship (most early heels were actually heavy platforms) often prohibited walking without assistance. A servant's arm or a sedan chair were required to save the day, further accentuating the heightened position of the person with elevating footwear. This is probably the reason why high heels are almost exclusively associated with women today. The high heel reflects the image of the pedestal, a position to which women have been relegated, with both ennobling and crippling results, throughout much of history.

The high heel exaggerates the curve and motion of the thighs and buttocks, creating a provocative visual impression. Although, when carried off with grace and control, the visual effect of high heels is undeniably attractive, they do inhibit freedom. As with many beautification practices, wearing high heels exacts a price.

Honey

Honey is a sweet, thick, syrupy substance that bees make as food from the nectar of flowers. It has been used in cosmetics since Egyptian times. Greek philosophers referred to honey as the secret of eternal youth. Honey is one of the most effective natural humectants, that is, a hydrophilic, or water-loving, substance that attracts moisture from the air. Without a humectant to help retain moisture, cosmetics would quickly dry up and cake, making them impossible to spread. As a skin freshener, experts recommend a mixture of raw honey and lemon juice for oily skin and raw honey and milk for dry skin.

See also: FACIALS

Hormones

Hormones are chemical regulators released into the bloodstream by the endocrine glands. These glands, located throughout the body, affect every aspect of growth and development. Hormones attach themselves to the nerve endings of receptor proteins designed to receive them. These proteins reside in certain target cells scattered through the body and activate a series of chemical reactions. Dramatic changes in body chemistry, as a result of hormonal activity, occur during puberty and, for women, during pregnancy, menopause, and menstruation. These internal changes in chemistry have physical and emotional side effects. The most obvious manifestations of this turmoil appear on the skin. During adolescence, because of raging hormonal activity, it is especially important to take proper care of the skin to reduce the chances of developing severe acne. Hormone creams that contain estrogen are effective in healing aging skin and increase the skin's capacity to retain moisture. Some bodybuilders, sometimes with disastrous results, take hormone injections to increase their capacity to acquire bulk. Because hormones effect the entire endocrine system, they should be used with great care.

See also: ACNE, SKIN

Hydrotherapy

Water is a major constituent of all living things. It is Nature's great purgative. Water fuels and flushes out the human body. Hydrotherapy, or healing with water, works because the human skin, which is largely comprised of water, readily responds to moisture and because many nerve endings lie close to the skin's surface. These nerve endings respond differently to heat and cold. The localized application of hot water relaxes muscles and slows circulation. Cold water dilates constricted blood vessels, thereby increasing blood flow. Water evaporating inside the bloodstream helps wash and scrub arteries and restores lubrication and elasticity to the cholesterol-laden lifelines of the body.

Hydrotherapy was first introduced as a formalized process in Parisian salons and health spas. (The practice of using mineral water itself for medicinal and rejuvenating purposes is quite ancient.) It is a process that capitalizes on the magical properties of pure water as a solvent and transporter of nutrients into and wastes out of the body. Hydrotherapy is designed to improve circulation and increase the skin's absorption of moisture. It is also used as part of weight loss programs, to relieve tension, to improve the shape and texture of the breasts, and to stimulate milk supply for nursing mothers. Equipment can be purchased at drugstores for a modified at-home treatment. However, an initial taste of the benefits of hydrotherapy can be obtained by the habitual consumption of eight to ten glasses of purified water every day.

Hypoallergenic

Hypoallergenic products are those that are less likely to cause adverse reactions in persons with highly sensitive skin. The FDA publishes guidelines that specify the parameters of this term. Unlike words such as "natural" and "pure," there are restrictions governing the usage of "hypoallergenic" on cosmetic labels. This quality-control measure does not mean, however, that hypoallergenic products can cure pre-existing conditions. Furthermore, a substance utterly free of allergens is impossible to manufacture because for every substance in existence, somewhere there is an individual who is allergic to it. Severe allergic conditions should prompt consultation with a dermatologist.

See also: ALLERGENS

Ingredients in Cosmetics

Cosmetics are composed of a wide range of substances. Some cosmetics are entirely natural, numerous others are synthetic, and many contain a combination of ingredients. Cosmetic manufacturers are required to list the ingredients found in their products. It is important that consumers avail themselves of as much information as possible about the sources, uses, and effects of ingredients found in the cosmetic

products they commonly purchase. As consumers become more knowledgeable about the relative safety of cosmetic products, manufacturers
are pushed to develop products whose components and processes of
manufacture are more sensitive to human and environmental health as
well as beauty concerns.

The following is a list of some of the most common cosmetic ingredients, many of which are associated with skin allergies in some
people:

Acacia (also known as gum arabic) is the dried, gummy discharge
of the stem and branches of several species of the African acacia
plant. It is an odorless, slightly yellow, brittle solid usually ground
and dissolved in water for cosmetic preparations such as gels. It is
used to give body, or viscosity, to liquids so that insoluble ingredients
remain suspended.

Almond oil is used as a fragrance in some cosmetic products.

Alum is a mild astringent used in a wide range of products.

Aluminum sulphate is a white crystalline salt. It is used in purifying
water and fixing dyes.

Benzoin is a balsamic resin. In its natural form, it is used as a reducing
agent (see *Reducing agents*).

Borax is a softening agent that is moderately soluble in water. It is
found in soap and bath salts.

Boric acid is an odorless antiseptic, fungicide, and mild germicide
which, due to its soothing properties, is found in a number of medicinal
cosmetic products including eyewashes and antiseptic solutions. It is also
used in the manufacture of enamels, such as nail polish.

Carmine is a rich crimson pigment prepared from dried insects. It is
used to color lipsticks and rouges.

Cocoa butter is used as an emollient and as a lubricant for the skin.
This yellowish or white solid melts at body temperature and emits a
pleasant, chocolaty smell.

Coriander is an herb of the parsley family. Its aromatic fruit is used
for fragrance.

Cornstarch is used in some facial and baby powders. Persons who are
allergic to corn are usually allergic to cornstarch as well.

Cottonseed oil is pressed from the seeds of the cotton plant and found
in some soaps.

Eucalyptus is an aromatic evergreen plant. Its essential oil is used for perfume, as an antiseptic, and as an expectorant.

Formaldehyde is a colorless, pungent gas used in solution as a powerful disinfectant and preservative.

Glycerine, formed through the decomposition of fats, oils, or molasses, is a colorless, odorless, sweet, syrupy liquid used in cosmetic products for its skin-softening properties. Glycerine is found in lotions, soaps, facial creams, and cuticle creams.

Lanolin is the purified fat from the wool of sheep. It provides a protective covering for the skin and acts as a very efficient absorber of moisture. This is why it is found in many skin ointments and moisturizers.

Lemon is a citrus fruit whose oil is used as a flavoring or fragrance.

Linseed oil is a yellowish oil extracted from flaxseed, and used, because of its drying qualities, in the manufacture of oil paints and some oil-based cosmetics.

Orange oil is found diluted in many perfumes and colognes. The same substance is also used as a flavoring.

Paraffin is a mineral wax found in lipstick, hair preparations, and ointments.

Phenol is a crystalline compound produced from coal tar. It is used in making synthetic resins and antiseptics.

Preservatives are a crucial component in cosmetics. Before preservatives were developed, infections and illnesses from cosmetic products (not to mention food) was quite common. Preservatives prevent bacteria from developing inside containers. Paraben is one kind of preservative commonly used.

Reducing agents are a category of substances found in cosmetic products. A reducing agent removes oxygen from other substances, thereby reducing it. In the process, the reducing agent itself becomes oxidized, the complementary chemical reaction. Because reducing agents reduce the amount of oxygen in the skin tissues to which they are applied, they can destroy skin parasites that are dependent on oxygen for survival. Some reducing agents found in cosmetics include alcohol, glycerine, tar, and zinc.

Resorcinol is a synthetically produced crystalline compound used in making dyes and pharmaceuticals.

Rice starch and wheat starch are used in some facial powders.

Salicylic acid is a white, colorless powder with a faint wintergreen scent. It has antiseptic, deodorizing, and keratinous properties (the latter fortifies the protein found in hair and nails). It is frequently present in treatments for rheumatism.

Talc a mineral ground into fine dust for face and body powders.

Tallow is an animal fat used in manufacturing many soaps.

Wintergreen is an aromatic compound derived from the oil of this evergreen shrub. It is used as a flavoring and in some medicines.

Zinc chloride is a white, crystalline powder used as an antiseptic.

This list is by no means comprehensive, but it can be used to provide an introductory orientation. Every consumer would do well to adopt a critical attitude toward the beauty products he or she buys. Products used in such an intimate fashion—to grace, augment, refine, and alter our bodies—merit our scrupulous attention.

Wintergreen

Ionization

The tiny particles of matter identified as atoms are electrically charged, positively or negatively. When negative atoms are released into the atmosphere, they have a soothing effect on the skin. Ionization occurs naturally in unpolluted air, especially near bodies of water, mountains, and before a rainstorm. Ionized air ameliorates acne, burns, migraines, poor respiration, and mental fogginess. It also can be channeled to bleach or lighten irregular pigmentation and protect against premature aging of the skin. Ionization is used for deep penetration of the skin with water soluble creams. Trained cosmeticians use equipment such as ionta rollers and ionta masks to treat the skin directly. An ionizer, which artificially charges ions in the air, works to beautify the skin. Typically, this treatment is employed during sleep.

Jewelry

Whether as symbols of wealth and status, as elements of personal adornment, or as magical or religious objects, jewelry is as intricately connected with the history of humanity as fashion and cosmetics. From the most primitive to the most sophisticated, all human cultures have crafted rings, bracelets, necklaces, earrings, brooches, and their facsimiles from diverse materials, ranging from pieces of bone, pebbles, teeth, seeds, feathers, and shells to industrial materials such as plastics to precious metals and gems.

The Ancient Worlds. The ancient Egyptian, Assyrian, and Babylonian civilizations mastered many techniques still used in contemporary manufacture of jewelry, such as chiseling, molding, inlay, and granulation. The making of jewelry involved much skill and was as highly valued as any other art form. The wearing and making of jewelry was also part of religious practices in these civilizations. The splendidly crafted golden death masks of the pharaohs are still counted among the world's most impressive jewelry.

The ancient Greeks and later also the Etruscans of Italy refined the craft of working with metals to such a degree that for a long time other jewelers were unable to match their skills. The Romans, on the other hand, cared less for workmanship than for the value of the piece. They preferred heavy jewelry and used gems abundantly. They popularized finger rings for men as well as women. During the height of the Roman empire, many cultured citizens often wore one or even two rings on every finger.

The Modern World. Inspired by the excavation of Pompeii, Westerners in the late eighteenth century replaced the playful and complex Rococo style of jewelry with a highly structured classicism. Simple lines, strong balance, and purity of shape again became the standards for judging the beauty of jewelry. At this time, the simple, delicate cameo, with classical motifs cut in stone or shell, became very popular.

From about 1820 on, a return to more naturalistic patterns became fashionable. Flowers, leaves, and other organic elements reemerged as appropriate subjects. This tendency culminated in the Art Nouveau movement in the early twentieth century. During this period, an eclectic historicism was evident; jewelers began to move more or less arbitrarily from one historical style to another as each individual project demanded.

The Industrial Revolution in the second half of the nineteenth century also influenced the nature of jewelry. Industrial production made a wider distribution of jewelry possible but threatened the skilled workmanship of jewelers. As early as the 1860s, small machine parts were incorporated into the design of jewelry. It took World War I to introduce what is today a staple piece of jewelry for men and women—the wristwatch.

Today, we have much more liberal ideas about what constitutes acceptable jewelry. Precious stones and metals are still, because of their scarcity, seen as valuable. However, even in the world of high fashion, the playful spirit of seeing potential jewelry in everything— from papier-mâché, feathers, beads, brass, and synthetic materials to safety pins—reflects a deeper change in our attitude toward the world at large. This attitude is simultaneously more conspicuous and more down-to-earth, more theatrical and less metaphysical, and certainly more democratic.

See also: COSMETICS, EGYPT, FASHION

Jojoba Oil

Jojoba (*Simmondsia californica*), also called "goat nut," is a wild desert plant native to California. It is a sturdy, many-branched shrub with leathery, oblong leaves and acornlike seeds that grow in clusters. Experiments in the last few decades have revealed that the oil from these seeds can be used as a substitute for the rare and expensive oil from sperm whales. Jojoba oil is used as a lubricant for high-speed machinery and as an ingredient in furniture polishes, floor and car waxes, as well as in cosmetics. In recent years jojoba oil has become almost a fad ingredient—the universal element of a whole range of beauty products. Jojoba oil works as a moisturizer and adds a subtle fragrance. It is found in shampoos, conditioners, skin creams, and lotions. In hair products it helps restore the hair's original natural sheen, body, and strength. Jojoba oil slows hair loss, dissolves sebum embedded in the scalp, aids in arresting dandruff, and stimulates the scalp, promoting hair growth. It is almost hard to believe that so many advantageous uses have been found for the berries of a wild roadside bush!

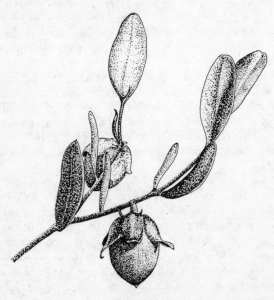

Jojoba

Kama Sutra

The *Kama Sutra* is an ancient Indian text on erotics that outlines the sixty-four arts of seduction to be cultivated by men and women of the upper classes. It was composed in the early centuries of what was the Christian epoch in the Western world, and its authorship is attributed to the sage Vatsyayana.

Although the *Kama Sutra* is a secular text, it demonstrates the reverence Indian culture attached to the pursuit of sensuality and beauty in many different manifestations. In addition to instructions on erotic techniques (such as the fine points of sixteen different kinds of kisses) it provides recipes for aphrodisiacs and love potions and guidelines for tattooing, painting the body, and coloring the hair, teeth, and nails. Men are instructed to bathe every morning, clean their teeth, anoint their bodies with perfume, rinse their eyes with collyrium (an eyewash made from anise seeds), dab lips with red lac (a resinous substance secreted on certain trees by insects), stand quietly in front of a mirror for a few moments, and finally, chew on a betel quid to sweeten the breath. A young gentleman was expected to rub his body with oil every other morning, shave his face every fourth day and the entire body every fifth or tenth day.

Kelp

Kelp is the general name for large brown seaweed. Kelp is a distinctive and useful ingredient in various natural beauty products because of its numerous healing properties. Natural cosmetics made with kelp produce smooth skin, shiny hair, and sturdy fingernails.

Kelp has a high silicon content. Silicon is believed to keep skin from sagging and wrinkling. For this reason, seaweed extract (derived from kelp) is found in natural cleansing creams, soaps, and massage lotions.

Seaweed lotions are used in dieting programs in Spain because seaweed is considered to have anticellulite properties.

Because seaweed is rich in protein, kelp shampoos and conditioners exhibit a penetrating moisturizing action enriching hair which is itself protein. An ancient folk beauty treatment (still employed in Japan) entails boiling seaweed in water and then using the water as a hair rinse to invigorate hair roots.

Kelp (in micronized form) is an important element in thalassotherapy, the therapeutic use of seawater herbs including seaweed, sea ware herb, and sea salts. A hot seaweed bath improves skin elasticity by stimulating blood circulation and eliminating toxins from the body through the sweat glands.

In addition, powdered kelp, in small doses, can be taken internally to cleanse the digestive system, tone the walls of blood vessels, and normalize thyroid gland activity. Because of its high iodine content, it stimulates the thyroid and acts to remedy obesity. Furthermore, kelp is highly nutritious; it contains vitamins A, B complex, C, and E, as well as calcium, sulfur, iron, and copper.

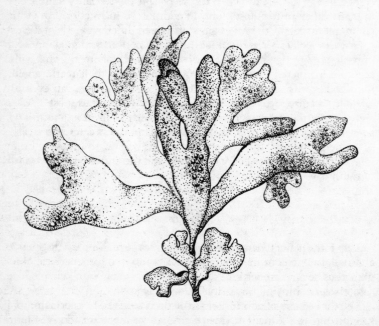

Seaweed

Lactic Acid

Lactic acid, produced by bacterial fermentation, is the chemical source of most tooth decay. It is a yellow or clearish, syrupy acid produced in the mouth by the fermentation of lactose (found in dairy products and crystallized sugar). Enzymes contained in saliva act on lactose to produce lactic acid. Lactic acid is produced in the process of digesting some carbohydrates and all sucrose (crystalline sugar extracted from sugar cane and sugar beets). Lactic acid normally takes time to produce, but sugar behaves like a catalyst in the mouth. Soft foods laden with refined sugar greatly increase the volume and speed with which lactic acid is produced.

See also: TEETH

Lanolin

Lanolin is the purified fat derived from sheep's wool. It protects the skin and facilitates the absorption of skin ointments. Lanolin is manufactured in two forms: anhydrous (without water) and hydrous (25 to 30 percent water). When lanolin is completely free of water it appears as a transparent, brownish-yellow glutinous mass. Since it is difficult to manipulate in this state, it is usually mixed with liquid petroleum to make its application to the skin easier. When mixed with other fats, lanolin will absorb up to 300 percent water. In a hydrous form, lanolin forms a soft, white mass.

Because of the similarity between lanolin and the fatty secretion of human skin, and lanolin's effectiveness as a conductor of liquids into the skin, it is often found as an ingredient in moisturizing lotions.

Legs

"He stands alone at the door of his home,
with his long-legged heart in his hand."
 —Dylan Thomas

Legs have always attracted the human imagination. Frank Mayfield, author of a text on the history of department stores, is correct in his assessment that "legs are staples and will never go out of fashion while the world lasts."

Riddles involving the legs are the oldest known to exist. The riddle that Oedipus solved to defeat the Sphinx was: "What goes by four legs in the morning, two in the afternoon, and three at night?" The answer is, of course, "man." Legs in Egyptian hieroglyphics stood for elevation and erections.

Perhaps the use of legs as symbols has something to do with humanity's evolution. Our development into a bipedal, or upright, two-legged creature marked a crucial turning point. Walking on two limbs instead of four meant that the ancestors of *Homo sapiens* could see farther into the distance instead of focusing mostly on the ground directly below. In a sense, the ability to look forward provided the evolutionary pressure necessary to create the concept of a future. Humans became conscious of literally moving through time toward something beyond the horizon.

But legs are admired for their beauty as well as the mobility they provide. Over the centuries, as the fashionably acceptable length of the skirt has shortened in the West, beautiful legs have become a greater concern among women. Interestingly, the most common problems that beset Westerners' legs are virtually unknown in less developed cultures. Varicose veins are not the inevitable result of age. They are the result of poor circulation and weak muscle tone. Circulation in the legs is inhibited by long-term obesity, inactivity, and standing up for extended periods of time. Blood vessels need the support provided by well-toned muscles. Muscle toning exercises are the best preventive for varicose veins. During pregnancy, when the pressure on the legs is increased, exercise is even more crucial. Persons with occupations that require standing for long stretches should wear support hose; however, they should not be worn at all times as they inhibit muscle formation. Certain vitamins are useful as both preventives and treatments of varicose veins: vitamin C contains antiinflammatory properties; vitamin E works to break up blood clots.

Aside from varicose veins, impaired circulation in the lower body can lead to thick ankles and overdeveloped thighs. In addition to exercise and improved diet, localized massage performed regularly is helpful for reshaping the legs. A surgical procedure known as lateral thigh lipectomy is now performed by plastic surgeons. This is an involved procedure wherein fat is literally suctioned out of the legs. However, it is an expensive, painful process and the bulges may reappear if one's life-style is not changed.

The legs comprise half of the height of an average adult. It is important to nurture the texture as well as the shape of such a vast portion of one's anatomy. Smooth skin can be cultivated by the regular (at least several times weekly) removal of dead skin cells from the surface. Use a sloughing product and a loofah sponge. Afterward, apply a conditioning lotion or cream.

The removal of hair from the legs is an ancient practice, originally employed by both men and women. But today more and more women are rejecting this time-consuming activity, particularly in Europe. One option to removal is bleaching the hair with a hydrogen-peroxide paste. But if a smooth surface is desired, there are several methods for accomplishing this end. The most short-term means of hair removal is shaving. Some longer lasting processes use depilatories and wax—which can be performed in special salons or at home. Electrolysis is the only permanent means of hair removal and must be done professionally.

Beautiful legs are impossible without healthy feet. Avoid ill-fitting shoes and other forms of neglect of the body's foundation.

See also: ELECTROLYSIS, FEET

Lemon

The lemon is the most popular fruit used in beauty products. Lemon juice is used in masks, moisturizers, and acne products. Because it is highly acidic, lemon juice can be used as a hair rinse to dissolve the alkaline film that shampoos often leave behind. Likewise because of its acidic properties, lemon rind, rubbed against the teeth, removes dark stains (but should be rinsed off thoroughly afterward so that the acid does not destroy tooth enamel). Lemon juice bleaches out skin discolorations, especially on the hands. It is also effective as an astringent to clean pores of grime, speed up the skin's metabolism, and relax facial muscles. But because lemons are 7 percent citric acid, their juice should never be used without diluting it first with water.

Drinking lemon juice, a major source of vitamin C encourages the growth of healthy connective tissues (which comprise ligaments, cartilage, and veins) by bringing hydrogen to the red blood cells.

Lemon

How to Use a Lemon Juice Rinse

- Juice two lemons and dilute the liquid with the same amount of water.
- Wash hair with an alcohol-free shampoo; rinse thoroughly.
- Pour lemon mixture over hair, massaging it into hair and scalp.
- Leave the lemon rinse on for a few minutes and then rinse completely.

Liposuction

The technical term for liposuction, or fat removal surgery, is suction lipectomy. It is one of the most difficult and problematic types of cosmetic surgery available today. This complex procedure leaves major scars, is expensive, and requires an extended hospital stay and recuperation time. If it is performed incorrectly, severe muscle or nerve damage can result.

A lipectomy can only be performed on persons of otherwise normal body weight who have stubborn fat deposits in specific areas. The surgeon makes an incision in the region and inserts a small, thin curette attached to metal tubing with a suction device. The fat is literally sucked out. It is highly preferred to achieve the same results with exercise and dieting if possible. The statistics surrounding this procedure suggest that it is wise to investigate this option thoroughly before committing to it. Thorough research begins with the choice of a highly qualified surgeon.

See also: COSMETIC SURGERY

Lips

Lips have a unique construction that gives them their color and sensitivity. Although blood is supplied in abundance to the entire second layer of the skin, in the lips this layer is covered only by a thin, transparent, mucous membrane. This is why the lips are red. The thinness of the mucous membrane heightens the sensitivity of the region; the lips are one of the most sensitive areas of the body. Lips, more so than the surrounding skin of the face, are vulnerable to weather conditions, excessive moisture (e.g., repeatedly licking the lips), and abrasive action, such as biting the lips. Oil- and petroleum-based moisturizers, balms, creams, and lipsticks help seal moisture in the lips and inhibit continuous wetting that aggravates chapped lips.

Nature has developed the shape of the lips to allow for drinking and grasping food, but the lips have been a focal point of beauty as well because of their sensuous shape. Sigmund Freud fancied that the lips suggest the female sexual organ. Whether or not most would agree with this explicit metaphor, they would acknowledge the allure of the lips. The lips are the instrument of one of the most precious human activities—the kiss. Although scientists would find it difficult to prove that kisses are "sweeter than wine," any lover can attest that a kiss from the beloved can, as Christopher Marlowe writes in *The Tragic History of Doctor Faustus*, "suck forth [the] soul." Anthropologist Desmond Morris, author of *The Naked Ape*, claims that the lips even swell and redden in response to sexual arousal.

In many African, Brazilian, and even some North American tribes the endurance of excruciating pain in seeking to distort the size of the lips is common. Larger, or at least fuller, lips are the dominant historical preference, although petite, Cupid's bow or rosebud lips experienced a brief popularity in the Victorian era. Many cultures have dismissed downturned lips as the only genuinely ugly possibility, yet the lips of

Greta Garbo turn decidedly downward. This demonstrates the importance of evaluating individual features in terms of the entire face.

In cultivating the beauty of the lips, refrain from exaggerating their
size or altering their shape considerably. An extreme example of such
a project, with its simultaneously pathetic and comical results, is demonstrated on faces among the Ainu women of Japan who endured a
painful tattooing process to exaggerate the lips virtually from ear to
ear.

See also: LIPSTICK, MOUTH

Lipstick

The earliest lip paint dates back to 3500 B. C. It was made by the
Mesopotamians from a base of white lead. In advanced civilizations,
before manufactured lipstick was readily available to the general populace, many women resorted to sucking on lemons which they carried
around in a pocket, or else they surreptitiously bit their lips in order to
induce a redder hue. Women living among the New England Puritans
who frowned on the use of cosmetics would secretly prepare and administer lip balms from crushed rose petals. In Paris in 1910 lipstick was
first introduced in cartridge form. It was being produced in America by
1915. Now it is the most commonly used and frequently purchased
cosmetic on the market.

When modern lipstick first became socially acceptable, only bold colors were worn. An historical advertising campaign launched in 1952 by
Revlon inaugurated a new era in cosmetics, particularly lipstick. Revlon
introduced a product line called Fire and Ice. It was a lipstick-nail polish
combination that promised sex appeal and glamour. Later, during the
sixties and early seventies, more natural shades gained popularity. Now
a vast array of colors is available to most consumers.

Most lipsticks are made with castor oil, beeswax, perfume, flavoring,
and pigment. The colored, molten wax is poured into metal casings and
then subjected to a series of temperature tests. The product is then put
through a "flaming" process; that is, the lipstick is sent down a conveyor
belt where it rolls through tiny flames at high speed. The outer surface
of the wax melts and dries, creating a shiny finish.

Manufacturers expend a great deal of energy developing provocative
names and packages and producing innovative colors. Originally, color
was acquired by crushing the likes of berries and geranium leaves!
"Pearlized" lipstick was first made with fish scales. Now manufacturers
use an artificially produced silvery substance that reflects light. Modern

laboratories still borrow colors from nature, but produce them far more efficiently than the way nature produces them.

Even though major cosmetic manufacturers produce more than twenty thousand individual lipsticks daily, each batch is examined for bacterial contamination. Also, the color and texture are matched to prototypes to ensure standardization.

Painting the lips, especially in shades of red, is a seemingly universal practice. Anthropologist Desmond Morris claims that this is a feature of human evolutionary development. *Homo sapiens*, unlike the lower primates, prefer to couple face-to-face; the reddening of the lips may have acted as an early stimulant to encourage this increased level of intimacy by echoing the female genital lips (labia). In any case, painting the lips is a very ancient practice traceable back to the origins of humanity.

Choosing and Applying Lipstick. Lipsticks should be chosen to match one's natural coloring. Dramatic colors can be great fun, but they are not generally appropriate for everyday wear. Muted beige-pink or soft salmon tones are more likely to be flattering in everyday contexts. Four or five different shades should serve for regular use, while distinctive colors should be acquired to complement special outfits. Older women should avoid frosted lipsticks as they tend to accentuate the wrinkles on the lips. The transparency of glosses makes them appropriate for younger women and others who wish to give subtle color and moisture to the lips without defining the shape.

Although it is common to apply lipstick directly from the tube, lipstick should always be applied with a lip brush. Trace a definite outline for the lips first. Lip pencils are especially designed for this purpose. Subtle changes in the shape of the mouth that resist smearing may be achieved by adjusting the natural line of the lips with a pencil. After tracing the perimeter, fill the interior surface of the lips with a brush. Blot lips with a tissue after application is complete. Do not press the upper and lower lips together. Top and bottom lips are not the same size, so this will only defeat the attempt to acquire a clean shape. One can add fullness to the lips by applying a bit of white eye shadow to the middle of the lower lip. To reduce the lips, use a slightly darker tint in the middle of both lips and a lighter tint on the outside.

See also: LIPS

Loofah Sponge

The loofah is a dry, course gourd that softens when it is submerged in water. It is used for exfoliation (the removal of dead cells from the surface of the skin) and to stimulate circulation. It is sold in its natural state, cut into mitten form, or attached to terry cloth for more convenient scrubbing. Using a loofah sponge benefits the entire body except for the tender skin of the face.

Loofahs can be purchased at natural food stores, drugstores, and in the toiletry departments of some major chain stores.

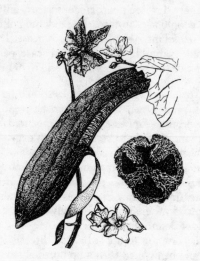

The loofah plant grows very fast and produces club-shaped gourds which are peeled and dried.

Lotions

The term "lotion" is applied to a wide variety of products designed to serve different cosmetic needs. There are lotions that act as cleansers, astringents, acne medications, and complexion softeners. However, lotions are most commonly known as moisturizers. Some ingredients that have gone into the manufacture of lotions for centuries are coconut milk, rosewater, and lanolin. These are still among the most popular elements in moisturizers today.

Mammoplasty (Cosmetic Breast Surgery)

Mammoplasty is cosmetic surgery to alter the size of the breasts. There are two types of procedures: augmentation and reduction. Breast augmentation is the most common as well as the simpler of the two. Over 100,000 silicone implant operations are performed in the United States per year. Formerly, doctors administered injections of liquid silicone however, this frequently caused infection, inflammation, and scarring and is now illegal. The operation now performed involves implants made of a saline solution of silicone gel. Implants come in a range of eight different sizes; they are inserted by way of incision. The procedure requires a three- to five-day hospital stay, several weeks of recuperation, and the extended wearing of a special support bra. Contemporary implants do not harden as older prostheses did, but breasts will not flatten out against the chest when lying down as natural breasts do.

Women with massive breasts that cause posture defects, shortness of breath, and backaches may consider reduction surgery. This is a far more complex procedure, with an actual operation time of three to five hours. It is not recommended for women who are simply overweight. Note: This procedure is performed to reduce the enlarged male breast as well.

See also: COSMETIC SURGERY

Manicure

The word manicure is derived from the Latin word *manus*, meaning "hand." Manicures range from cleaning and trimming the fingernails to highly complex, luxurious affairs offered at exclusive beauty and health spas. Many people perceive well-manicured nails as an essential emblem of success and status as well as beauty. But manicures are also healthful. In addition to improving the appearance of the hands, manicures can improve poor circulation.

The fingernails deserve a manicure treatment once a week. However, most people can neither afford the time nor expense of visiting a salon this frequently. With the right supplies, an effective manicure can be performed at home.

Modern nail cosmetics did not become available until the early twentieth century. Cuticle remover came on the market first, followed by liquid nail enamel. An opaque polish was introduced in 1938, which meant that cosmeticians could begin to design polishes to match lipsticks. Products are available now that are designed to strengthen the nails. They are usually made with silicone. Some nail polishes will also, over time, help to strengthen weak nails.

Nail colors should be chosen to coordinate with lip colors and clothing. Remove chipped and streaked polish promptly. Nail bleaches, specially formulated for this sensitive region, remove stains such as ink spots. Do not apply new coats over previous applications, even if it is the same color and the old coat appears to be smooth. Most complete manicure kits include the following: nail brush, emery boards, file, manicure scissors, cuticle pusher, cotton swabs, buffer, cuticle cream, base coat of a neutral color, polish remover, and sealer.

See also: HANDS, NAILS

How to Do a Home Manicure

- Clean the hands thoroughly. Remove any stains, such as ink stains, with cream bleach.

- Massage the hands while applying a moisturizing lotion. Clean under the nails with an orangewood stick—do not use a metallic instrument.

- File nails to conform with the shape of the fingertips. Use an emery board or diamond file, making strokes in a single direction. Smooth rough edges by placing the file perpendicular to the nail and making slow, steady downward strokes.

- Lubricate cuticle area with cuticle cream. Carefully push the skin back from this area and cut excess skin with nail scissors.

- Apply base coat to nails and let dry. Apply polish. Remove excess from the sides of the nails with a polish remover. Finish off with a sealer on top and below the tips of the nails. Apply all coats with single, upward strokes from nail base to tips.

- After the polish is dry, moisturize the hands again. Some removers have drying effect on the skin and besides, it is virtually impossible to overmoisturize the hand.

Marie Antoinette

Marie Antoinette (1755–1793), queen of France from 1774 until she was executed by guillotine twenty years later, is remembered by most people for her callousness toward the poor, an attitude that fueled the anger of the revolutionaries against the monarchy. After being informed that the peasants were rioting in the streets because they had no bread, she responded with her infamous retort: "Let them eat cake." She was also famous for her resplendent beauty. Sadly, this beauty was virtually destroyed in a few short years under the strain imposed by the political upheaval of the time. Many people do not know, however, that early in their marriage, Marie Antoinette was criticized by her husband Louis XVI for failing to pay proper attention to her appearance. She then hired a consultant named Jeanne Bertin, called Rose, whose other clients included the tsarina of Russia and the Queens of Sweden and Spain. During her tenure, Rose was paid more than the secretary of state for her advice and administrations as a beauty consultant.

Marie's Secret

Legend has it that just before Marie Antoinette was sent to the guillotine she revealed the secret of her lovely skin to a lady-in-waiting. Presumably, every morning (until she was imprisoned in the Bastille, that is) she treated her skin with a special tonic. You can recreate her ritual:

- Add a few drops camphor essence to a basin of water.
- Splash onto skin and pat dry.

The camphor will medicate blackheads and tighten overly large pores, giving the complexion a smooth, seamless appearance. Another benefit of camphor is its aromatic, woody fragrance that repels insects!

Marketing Beauty

> *"What's in a name?"*
> —Juliet in Shakespeare's
> *Romeo and Juliet*

The verbal and visual language of advertising plays a significant role in the generation of value. The way in which a product is marketed, the associations conjured up by the product's name and the images used to sell it, often have more to do with how it is received than any intrinsic value it may have.

In general, language plays a crucial role in defining and shaping the self-perception of human beings. The degree to which people perceive something as beautiful is greatly influenced by what it is called and how it is described in words. Words have color, texture, music, fragrance, and complex connotations as well as denotations. A single word can trigger a wealth of imaginative, sensory associations. Because French is a beautiful language and because it operates in a culture that is intimately associated with romance and the refinement of beautiful things and people, products with French names generally appeal to the aesthetic imagination.

In today's world, elegance and sophistication are associated with simplicity. This is a result of the influence of high-tech and abstract designs in art, architecture, and fashion, styles that are generally inaccessible to all but the economically or intellectually elite. Therefore, some high-status products bear very simple names. A name utterly devoid of frills such as Chanel No. 5 and Y, two fragrances that appeal to the upper income bracket, are indicative of this trend.

In a health-conscious age, products that boast natural or organic ingredients and/or medical approval also have a positive connotation. "Natural" is a word that implies a closeness to and respect for the earth. "Artificial" sounds less attractive. However, the distinction between things that are termed natural and those termed artificial is often difficult to determine. Nevertheless, it is incontrovertible that consumers are more comfortable reading ingredients like almond oil, aloe vera, or rainwater on cosmetic labels rather than ammonia, formaldehyde, and stearic acid.

The language used in cosmetic advertising is regulated for consumer protection. In the United States, the Federal Trade Commission works to prevent misleading or false claims from appearing in magazines, newspapers, and on radio and television. Many cosmetic firms belong to the

Cosmetic, Toiletry and Fragrance Association (CTFA) which works in cooperation with the Federal Food and Drug Administration (FDA). Members of the CTFA voluntarily submit lists of product ingredients and report any consumer complaints they receive to the FDA.

See also: FOOD AND DRUG ADMINISTRATION (FDA), NATURAL COSMETICS

Mascara

See: EYE MAKEUP

Masks

See: FACIALS

Massage

"Massage" comes from the Arabic word *massa*, which means to stroke or to touch. Most people experience a natural impulse to massage parts of their own body when they are in pain. An awareness of the connection between massage and healing is ancient. The Greeks practiced massage as a cure for many ailments. Almost every culture has developed techniques for "healing by touch." The two systems of massage most commonly practiced today emerged from two very different cultures. One is the Swedish method of muscle manipulation; the other is the Eastern meridian system which uses a knowledge of crucial pressure points on the body (shiatsu). Regular massage treatments lead to a more radiant complexion, slow the aging process, indirectly tone muscles, alleviate puffiness, and increase one's ability to concentrate through relaxation.

Relieving tension, improving circulation, and beautifying the skin are three principal benefits of massage. A body burdened with tension cannot achieve its full aesthetic as well as functional potential. Tense muscles operate inefficiently and inhibit proper circulation. Massage stimulates blood circulation; blood in turn nourishes the tissues of the body. Therefore, the organs of the body function more smoothly and wastes are eliminated more promptly. Massage is also one of the most efficient and healthful means of alleviating stress available. Massage, quite literally, calms the nerves. Furthermore, massaging action warms the skin, causing perspiration and an increased production of sebum. This helps maintain the moisture content of skin cells and also speeds the removal of debris from the surface of the skin.

Mental Health

" . . . nothing has so marked an influence on the direction of a man's mind as his appearance, and not his appearance itself, so much as his conviction that is attractive or unattractive."

—Leo Tolstoy, "Childhood"

The admiration for and pursuit of beauty is an essential part of a healthy life. Motivational research has demonstrated that people purchase and wear cosmetics not so much for sex appeal as for social acceptance and a sense of community. Scientists find that most people, a majority of the time, offer beautiful people preferential treatment. Appearance is the most obvious and most difficult-to-hide aspect of a human being and this is why it is used by many—fairly or unfairly—as an initial means of judging character.

People who perceive themselves as homely generally have low self-esteem. This suggests that beauty is also an attitude, a state of being that extends below the surface. Viewing oneself as unattractive can become a self-fulfilling prophecy. This is why a self-confident individual who actively pursues personal beauty is more likely to be perceived as beautiful by others than an insecure individual with more abundant natural gifts. As long as it does not become obsessive and interfere with the ability to lead a well-rounded existence, pursuing personal beauty is a crucial part of balanced mental health. Sociologists and psychiatrists assert that one indication of mental illness is inattention to personal grooming. The desire to appear more attractive for oneself and others is a healthy, cross-cultural, instinctual drive.

Middle Ages
(Eleventh to Fifteenth Centuries)

The Middle Ages, or medieval period, was the point in Western history between the time of classical civilization and the Renaissance. Although it is problematic to give the exact year of its birth and demise, reputable scholars often give it a life span from the fall of the Roman Empire (about 476) up to about 1450. Religion dominated the lives of most people during this period, and the pursuit of beautification of the soul dominated that of the body.

However, a concern with personal beauty did persist independently of the church. Fragrant oils were used profusely, although bathing was frowned upon as people believed it to be both immodest and a health risk! Women in the Middle Ages subjected themselves to bleedings in order to acquire a fashionable pallor. Leek juice was used to prevent hair loss. In English universities at this time, medicine and cosmetology were combined subjects. A student of these subjects, Andrew Bourde, wrote a book entitled *Brenyary of Health* wherein he recommends wiping the face with a scarlet cloth, while avoiding washing it often, in order to acquire healthy skin.

The Middle Ages also produced notions of an ideal beauty. Because the number seven was perceived as magical, the human face was divided into seven sections. The desired proportion of each section was determined relative to other facial features. For example, the width of the face was supposed to equal the length of two noses. Medieval artwork, although largely sacred in subject matter, nonetheless offers evidence of two widely different feminine ideals. One was the earthy, robust maternal figure, and the other was the delicate, romantic virgin for whom the crusading knights pined. The cult of the Virgin Mary, with its celebration of the immaculate conception—a femininity untouched by sexuality—came into being during this time and was a major influence in the division of female beauty into these two ideals.

See also: COSMETICS

Mirrors

> *"There are two ways of spreading light: to be the candle or the mirror that reflects it."*
> —Edith Wharton, *Vesalius in Zante*

> *"Mirrors should reflect a little before throwing back images."*
> —Jean Cocteau, *Des Beaux-Arts*

As fairy tales such as "Snow White" teach us, mirrors tell the truth. Although the truth is sometimes painful, human beings have an obsessive need to seek it out. Mirrors are symbolic of this search.

Before modern mirrors were available, many societies developed creative ways to allow people to see their images. A form of mirror has been unearthed from Egyptian tombs that dates back to 2800 B.C. In ancient Greece, mirrors were seen as fertility charms and were presented as gifts. Polished metal mirrors became available in Europe in the Middle Ages. They had some influence on the gradual increase in concern with personal appearance among the general populace. Historians consider the reawakening of interest in personal adornment as one factor that helped pull Europe out of the Dark Ages, a period largely characterized by massive neglect and poor health. The American Indians used sheets of mica or still pools of water.

The mirror itself is a contradictory symbol. It stands not only for introspection and truth through self-knowledge but also for vanity. In *The Dictionary of Symbols and Imagery*, mirrors are said to represent virginity to some cultures and lust to others. While mirrors are considered essential to the functioning of most households, they are surrounded by the folklore of superstition. There is a clearly discernible logic underlying the association between a broken mirror and ill health: a mirror's function is to report on a person's well-being; for an individual in a pantheistic culture (one that perceives the acts of divine beings in every event), the implication of a broken mirror was that the body has a rough path up ahead. The distressful period was set at seven years because of the Roman belief that a person's health changed in seven-year cycles. There is, after all, some factual basis for this assumption because the body's chemical makeup does change entirely every seven years. This ancient belief has stubbornly persisted; some people still quake in the face of a cracked mirror. Other folklore claims that mirrors absorb the souls of those who stare at them too long. On the other hand, to be a mirror metaphorically is to be of great import. For example, many, such as the Naturalist school of painting define art as the mirror of life. In any case, the mirror, like any other tool for beautification, can be both a blessing and a curse.

Moisturizer

The first somewhat refined skin moisturizer was invented by Galen of Pergamum, a Greek physician who lived in the second century. It was probably made of olive oil and beeswax. Many primitive societies, including American Indian tribes, used a basic "cold cream" made of animal fat to protect their skin against harsh weather and as a base for body paint. Over the centuries, many interesting homemade concoctions have been developed to soften the skin. The ancient Romans, mixed flour and milk. Isabeau of Bavaria, the consort of King Charles

VI of France in the early fifteenth century, frequently applied to her face an emollient of boar brains, wolf blood, and crocodile glands. She administered this cream as part of a magical ritual complete with incantations! In colonial America, women would sleep with strips of bacon across their faces in hopes of softening the skin, preventing wrinkles, and promoting blushing cheeks.

Cheeseborough Ponds created the first mass-produced cold cream. It was originally advertised as a good remedy for constipation, head colds, hay fever, malaria, syphilis, and typhoid, with its beneficial properties as a skin moisturizer thrown in as an afterthought.

Today the term "cold cream" is somewhat archaic. Products that accomplish the same tasks are more commonly called moisturizers. Moisturizers make sense for both men and women; skin dries out with age regardless of gender. The chief purpose of moisturizers is to hold water in the skin. Also, moisturizers are used to clean and soften the skin before applying makeup.

Application should start at the throat, working upward toward the scalp, rubbing in a circular motion. In preparation for bed, apply a layer of moisturizer/cold cream after washing the face. But in doing so, note that the skin will absorb all of the moisture it can within twenty to thirty minutes; therefore, it is unnecessary and even detrimental to retire for the night with a dense mask coating the face.

Montagu, Lady Mary Wortley

Lady Montagu (1689–1762) was an eighteenth century English writer. She is best known for her epistolary writings, although she was acknowledged as a distinguished, if minor, poet and essayist also. She wrote early feminist tracts and was affectionately dubbed "eccentric" by many who encountered her. In order to avoid an unwanted arranged marriage, she eloped with Edward Wortley Montagu who was a member of Parliament.

Montagu was appointed to a post in Turkey and Lady Montagu accompanied him. There she studied the cosmetic practices in harems and brought many samples back to England. She was the first Western woman to penetrate a Turkish bath and wrote provocative letters about the wonders she discovered there. In response to this experience, she remarked that, "If it were the fashion to go naked the face would be hardly observed." But because this was certainly not the fashion in priggish England, she did exert a sort amount of energy learning ways to beautify the face. Lady Montagu developed heavy plaster masks to conceal her pockmarked face which were taken up by her fellow countrymen. Later, she went to the heart of the matter and introduced the smallpox inoculation to England!

Montez, Lola

Lola Montez (1818–1861) was an international adventures who rose to fame on the coat tails of her beauty. Born in Ireland and christened Marie Dolores Eliza Rosanna Gilbert, she adopted "Lola Montez" as a stage name. She made her debut after only five months of dance training. Apparently, her dancing skills left much to be desired. However, her universally acclaimed beauty propelled her into stardom. In 1846, Louis I of Spain became completely infatuated with her after witnessing a performance. She became his mistress for a time. Also, the King of Bavaria was among her three husbands. She spent the latter part of her life in America, dancing as well as lecturing on feminine beauty and cosmetics. She claimed that beauty was best maintained through temperance, exercise, and cleanliness. For accomplishing this last, she recommended frequent lukewarm baths. She also made a point of bathing in milk every day motivated by the fallacy that milk would further whiten her lovely skin. Reputedly, her servants resold this milk to the dairymen after she was out of the tub!

Mouth

The mouth allows us to speak, eat, and breathe, and is the site of one of the most intimate human gestures: the kiss. There are twenty-one pairs of voluntary muscles and one involuntary muscle encircling the mouth. The roof of the mouth consists of the hard palate, the bony front region that separates the nose and mouth, and the soft palate at the rear, the curtain between the mouth and the pharynx (the back of the throat). The tongue, a flexible bundle of interwoven, striated muscles, helps us to eat, swallow, and speak.

In addition to being the center of such crucial activity as eating, drinking, breathing, kissing, singing, and speaking, the mouth is also a focal point of beauty. The acts of painting the lips, whitening the teeth, and sweetening the breath are universal beautification practices.

See also: BREATHING, LIPS, TEETH

Mud

The use of mud as a skin softener is quite ancient; mud packs were a staple of Egyptian beautification rituals, for instance. Even our hominid ancestors used mud packs to protect their skin from the scorching sun of the savannah. Today, the kind of mud found in most cosmetic facial masks is actually a high grade clay. Mud from certain regions, such as the south of England and the bottom of the Dead Sea (the lowest spot on the earth's surface), is rich in nutrients and has a medicinal effect on weather- and age-worn skin. In commercially developed mud packs, the clay (often kaolin and/or bentonite—produced by the decomposition of volcanic ash and capable of absorbing much water) is usually combined with distilled water, glycerin, zinc oxides, and fragrances. Mud/clay relaxes facial muscles, and gently tightens sagging skin, thereby softening lines and wrinkles. This type of facial—as well as the full-body mud bath—is very popular in European health spas.

See also: FACIALS

Nails

The chief purpose of the nails is to protect the tender skin of the fingertips and toes. Nails are composed primarily of a dry, dense protein known as keratin, plus 5 percent fat, which is actually hardened skin cells. The formation created by the accumulation of these skin cells at the sides and base of the nails is called the cuticle. Nails are hard because of their low water content. Because blood circulates at the nail base, or matrix, below the surface of the skin, nails grow even though they are made of dead matter. The white crescent at the base of the nail is called the lunula, from the word "luna," which means moon. It is white because these cells at the base are smaller and retain fewer nutrients.

Nails grow at an average rate of one millimeter per week, or about one sixth of an inch per month, their growth slowing in the summer and increasing in the winter. The nail of the middle finger grows fastest, and the thumbnail grows slowest. Toenails grow slower than fingernails, but toenails are thicker and sturdier. The rate of growth is also affected by hormonal changes, nutrition, general health, and age (nail growth slows with age).

Most problems with the health of nails are related to vitamin and mineral deficiencies. An iron deficiency can cause fragile, brittle nails. White spots on the nails are a result of zinc deficiency, or sometimes are the mark of minor injuries. These spots will grow out as the nail grows. Healthy circulation is crucial to healthy nails. The blood brings oxygen and nutrients, essentials for growth, to the nail base; if blood flow is sluggish, nails will be thin and short. The massage techniques and cuticle stimulation employed in manicures and pedicures dramatically improve circulation to the nails and, therefore, nail growth.

Another critical aspect of healthy, attractive nails is the appearance of the cuticle. Trim cuticles once a week. Cuticle cream should be applied regularly to lubricate the area. Before removing the cuticle, loosened it with an orangewood stick (cuticle pusher) or a reasonable, nonmetallic facsimile. Use manicure scissors to remove the cuticle gently. Afterward, apply a product that contains alcohol to the area.

See also: MANICURE, PEDICURE

Narcissus

Narcissus is the figure from Greek mythology who died pining away for his own beautiful reflection, thinking it was another person. This fate was imposed on him after he had resisted the advances of several females. He drove the wood nymph Echo mad with his beauty. She eventually wasted away so that only her plaintive voice remained.

Narcissus

Narcissus died on the banks of a spring where he was mesmerized by the image of his own countenance. The nymphs of the spring, although angry with him for slighting Echo, decided to prepare a special burial place to honor his tremendous beauty. However, during the preparation of the site, his body vanished and in its place the nymphs found a yellow-centered flower with white petals. The flowers now bear his name. In another myth, a garland of narcissus blossoms are given to the vindictive, avenging goddesses known as the Furies upon whom they have a calming effect. The classical Roman poet Ovid claimed that the bulbs of these flowers are good for removing skin blemishes.

By combining the features from these stories, insight into the nature of beauty is revealed. Narcissus's story is laden with implications about mankind's pursuit of the illusory—in Narcissus's case, an image rather than a person. However, tracing Narcissus's name back to its origins gives this traditional interpretation a deeper meaning. The linguistic root for the name Narcissus is the same as that for "narcotic," meaning stupor. Perhaps part of the message of this ancient story is that beauty has the power to cast one into a stupor. Attempts to maintain exclusive possession over a beautiful object or person, even one's own self, can prove disastrous.

Natural Cosmetics

The term "natural" is applied to substances that are not synthetic, that is, neither of human invention nor treated by chemical means. When the word natural is applied to cosmetics it usually means that these products contain substances found in, or produced by, nature.

It is virtually impossible to manufacture a product, especially one designed for wide-scale distribution, that is entirely "natural." Preservatives in cosmetics are necessary to protect the consumer's safety and pocketbook.

Some people distrust chemicals, often with good reason. However, anything that exists in the biological world is itself made of chemicals. A "chemical" substance is actually one that is more simple, or primitive, in structure. An "organic" substance such as the juice from an aloe vera plant, has a far more complex structure than a "chemical," such as sodium chloride (salt). But both are, of course, found in nature. "Natural" is sometimes used interchangeably with "organic." But "organic" specifically refers to a substance derived from something living. There are beneficial natural ingredients used in cosmetics that are inorganic, such as clay.

Many modern cosmetic manufacturers use the raw materials of the natural world to develop products. These include the essences and oils of fruits, vegetables, flowers, and herbs. Vitamins and proteins are also extracted from organic sources and used in the production of cosmetic products. Many consumers are attracted to products made with natural ingredients because they suggest greater healthfulness.

See also: INGREDIENTS IN COSMETICS, MARKETING BEAUTY

Neck

The neck is considered an erogenous zone by some cultures, which is why the neck is a favorite site for legendary vampire attacks. In West Africa, the ideal neck is one of two extremes, either noticeably fat and squat or long and swanlike. In the Sierra Leone, women wear rings between the chin and collarbone to elongate the neck. Ashanti women carry around dolls with long, slender necks during pregnancy in hopes that their babies will turn out likewise. The Padaung women of Burma artificially stretch their necks by wearing brass rings, increasing the numbers as they grow.

In the West, long, slender necks are associated with regal bearing. In

An Ashanti doll

fact, stretching the muscles of the neck with slow, carefully executed exercises improves posture and carriage, regardless of actual neck length. Neck stretches also relieve tension, relax facial muscles, lengthen the back, and invigorate blood circulation to the head. Men are more susceptible to weight gain in the region of the neck than women are, and it is one of the first places to show age in men.

Nutrition

The human body needs nourishment for two reasons. The first is to supply material to form new tissue, and the second is to supply energy for the running of the entire system. Proper nourishment is achieved in two parts through the intake of both the right kind of nutrients and sufficient caloric bulk.

Good nutrition is more complicated than merely having enough food to eat. For numerous busy people, a balanced diet is difficult to maintain. Also, many poorly informed people who eat substantial amounts of food are still malnourished because they do not get the essential nutrients. Furthermore, living in an affluent country does not guarantee that one understands or concerns oneself with nutrition. This assertion is easily supported by such statistics as the fact that 965,000 Americans drink Coca-Cola for breakfast.

A balanced diet does not mean "eating a little of everything available." The average American consumes nine pounds of chemical additives per year. These additives, like sugar, amount to "empty" calories. Calories are the body's fuel, but they only serve it well when the calories consumed provide fuel as well as nutrients. The human body needs about one dozen vital minerals, ten amino acids, approximately one dozen vitamins, a great deal of water, and a sufficient amount of carbohydrates, fats, and proteins. Raw fruits, vegetables, and nuts contain the biggest concentration of vitamins and minerals and greatly improve the elimination of wastes from the body. Roughage, or fiber, occurs naturally in these foods as well as in foods that must be cooked, such as brown rice and whole wheat. Raw, fibrous foods protect against wastes, even as they promote their elimination. Also, the body needs fewer quantities of raw than cooked foods to maintain a healthy status. Raw fruits, vegetables, and whole grains are known as unrefined complex carbohydrates, and unlike processed, high-concentration carbohydrates, they are metabolized slowly, thereby sustaining the body's energy level longer and more efficiently. A nutritious diet also requires foods that are low in fat, as well as little or no refined sugar and an abundance of natural spring water. Avoid overprocessed and refined foods and obvious pollutants such as caffeine, alcohol, and nicotine that throw the body's natural processes out of balance.

Researchers have linked illnesses such as coronary heart disease, tooth and gum decay, ulcers, diabetes, and varicose veins to the low-fiber, highly refined diet of Western civilized countries. The incidence of these illnesses has dramatically increased in the last fifty years in tandem with advancing technology for mass-producing "fast" food. These physical problems are virtually unknown in cultures outside the West, but they do develop in non-Western societies once a "civilized" diet has been introduced or when persons of different ethnic backgrounds move into a developed area and take up this kind of diet. Luckily, even as research makes it possible to produce and market more food that is inherently unhealthy, an awareness and knowledge of the value of nutrition is also on the rise.

Physical beauty depends upon what one consumes. Poor nutrition not only results in less energy and greater chances of illness but also usually means dull, lifeless hair, flaccid or blemished skin, brittle nails, and weight problems. Greater physical beauty through nutrition begins with detoxifying the body. Afterward, one must form and maintain new eating habits. A well-nourished body is livelier and more efficient. And, of course, physical vitality is a crucial quality of the beautiful individual.

See also: VITAMINS

Oatmeal

Oatmeal has been a favorite skin soother for centuries. Ladies of the eighteenth century French court often bathed in tubs filled with dry, milled oats to soften their skin before donning the elaborate costumes and cosmetics of the period. Oatmeal does actually work as a soap substitute. It is especially good for sensitive skin. Mixed with yogurt and milk, it creates a mask effective for tightening oily, sagging skin. Oatmeal can also be used as an ingredient in a total body scrub along with salt and a little margarine. Oatmeal is the mildest abrasive found in commercially produced soaps and scrubs.

Oatmeal

As food, natural, unadulterated oatmeal is one of the least expensive, most readily available, and vitamin-rich products around. Its potential for reducing cholesterol has recently come under scientific scrutiny.

See also: FACIALS

How to Make a Homemade Oatmeal Scrub

- Place two to three handfuls of rolled oats (the kind sold in bulk at health food stores) in a stocking leg.
- Knot it at the top.
- Use it to exfoliate the skin while bathing as you would a loofah sponge. The bag can be reused several times.

How to Make a Mask for Oily Skin

- Mix together sixteen ounces powdered oatmeal, eight ounces powdered almond meal (sold in natural foods stores), four ounces powdered orris root (sold in pharmacies), and one ounce powdered castile soap.
- Add two tablespoons of hot water. Mash the ingredients together into a thick paste.
- Apply to the face and neck, rubbing gently.
- Let it dry and leave it on for one hour.
- Rinse with cool water.

Obesity

Money-based societies in which food is not scarce tend to frown on fatness, whereas primitive agrarian societies in which food is less readily available see fatness as a kind of wealth. This irony is quite ancient. The prosperous Spartans forced plump children to exercise. Socrates, who lived in Athens during the Golden Age, danced every morning to keep thin. The vomitorium allowed illustrious Roman men to gorge and remain relatively thin.

Among the Bangwa and other African peoples obesity is prized by men and women as a sign of status. The chief must go through a nine-week fattening period at the beginning of his reign. All women submit to the same process for a seven- to nine-week period prior to marriage, after which they are publicly displayed by their new spouses with great pride. Other periods in Western culture have made a similar connection between prestige and body fat; today, however, the Western ideal is thinness. Even though about 25 percent of all Americans go on a diet every year, at present the average weight of American adults is much closer to obesity than desirable for physical health; one in four are actually classifiable as obese.

Obesity is undeniably unhealthy and greatly inhibits an individual's mobility and energy level. It greatly increases the odds of developing high blood pressure, varicose veins, arterial, liver, and kidney diseases, and chronic fatigue. The "ideal" weight is best defined as one that promotes maximum longevity. Women tend to be overweight sooner and in greater numbers than men, which means they also fall victim to fad diets in greater numbers. Obesity should be combated, but not by means of a fad diet. A sensible, regular exercise routine and a nutritional change in diet are the only means for effective slimming. Persons with serious weight problems should consult a physician for assistance in forming a personal weight-loss program.

Otoplasty (Cosmetic Ear Surgery)

Otoplasty is cosmetic surgery performed on the ears. Protruding ears are adjusted by removing stiff cartilage to bring them closer to the side of the head. Abnormally large ears can be reduced by making an incision in the outer part of the ears. People who feel their ears are problematic should consider altering their hairstyle to conceal the ears before resorting to surgery which is expensive and involves, as do all surgical procedures, pain.

See also: COSMETIC SURGERY

Ovid

"The art that adorns you should be unsuspected. Who but would feel a sensation of disgust if the paint on your face were so thick that it oozed down on your breast?"

—Ovid, *Ars Armatoria*

The legacy left by Ovid, the classical poet of ancient Rome, suggests that he was concerned with more than literary beauty. He wrote a voluminous text called the *Ars Armatoria* wherein he prescribes cosmetic beauty remedies for the men and women of his day. In this treatise, he explains that beauty can be acquired through care and lost through neglect. While this generalization is certainly wise, his specific recommendations are a bit daunting. For example, Ovid suggests bathing in egg whites to improve the skin, gluing on new eyebrows if a person's natural ones are too scanty, and lining the eyes with saffron, a yellowish powder, to make them appear larger. He encourages copious amounts of rouge and suggests a crocodile dung facial mask for improving the complexion. The latter, although not viewed as eccentric in his own culture, may suggest why Ovid is more aptly remembered today for his poetic retellings of the Greek myths than for his insights as a beautician!

Pedicure

In Latin, *pedicure* means "caring for the feet." The feet are among the most neglected portions of the human body. Regular pedicures can do wonders for improving one's general disposition and energy level. Also, healthy feet are attractive feet.

Many girls and women spend a considerable amount of time painting their toe- as well as fingernails. This practice may be a remnant from the older ritual of body painting, which remains a central feature in older societies, such as the Aboriginal culture. In varying degrees, humans have viewed many different body surfaces as canvases. As such, the flat, rigid plane of the toenails is, for some, an irresistible site for creative expression.

See also: FEET

How to Do a Home Pedicure

- Clean the feet and remove any old nail polish.
- Clip and file toenails straight across, moving the file in a single direction using steady strokes—do not hurriedly work the file back and forth.
- Moisturize the feet and rub rough spots, corns, or calluses with a pumice stone or callus file.
- Apply cuticle cream to the nails and use an orangewood stick to push the excess cuticle back.
- Give each foot a deep massage using body oil or lotion. Start at the instep, move up toward the toes, and then back to the heel and up around the ankle.

Perception

"Beauty is in the eye of the beholder."
—Margaret Hungerford,
Molly Brown

Perception is the manner in which sensory data are translated into mental understanding. Receptors located on the skin, in the eyes, ears, mouth, and nose send information to the brain where it is interpreted. Because all human beings have slightly different mechanisms for receiving and organizing the data, the tiniest experience is registered differently by every individual. No two people perceive an event in exactly the same way. If a group of observers is asked to describe an event, no two accounts will be identical. Vision scientists such as David Marr and Edwin Land have determined that the mechanisms of vision are organized in a tangled, hierarchical way, and what an observer sees and the ability to make sense of it is dramatically dependent on his or her prior questions, needs, and expectations. Far-ranging differences are likely even in descriptions of the most seemingly mundane incidents such as the arrival of a bus at a bus stop.

With abstract concepts such as what constitutes beauty, agreement is even less likely. In a study performed by psychologists Cross and Cross on the perception of facial beauty, a broad range of photographs of people were shown to a group who were asked to evaluate each one according to relative beauty. Not one photograph was completely overlooked. Even the least popular was chosen by a few judges as being very attractive. Most scholars agree that the qualities of a beautiful face in particular can never be defined completely.

Psychologist John Liggett explains that a large part of what a person registers as "real" is determined by individual perception. In other words, what a person is prepared to see to a large extent influences what he or she actually sees. Thus, we see the people we love as physically beautiful. Liggett also feels that the type of face that is somewhat ambiguous is the most likely to be perceived by the greatest number of observers as beautiful. He offers the faces of Greta Garbo and Ingrid Bergman as examples. Their faces have shadowy qualities that allow people to "project" specific ideals of beauty onto them. Ambiguity stimulates projection, the psychological process of ascribing one's feelings and attitudes onto an external entity. Projection is formed from a person's stockpile of memories. Familiarity, if it is comforting and appealing, breeds nostalgia. Nostalgia created from memories plays a major part in what a person experiences as beautiful. Faces that allow for a multiplicity of interpretations, like the face in Leonardo da Vinci's *Mona Lisa*, stimulate a wealth of personal associations. The more associations a work of art or a human face sparks in the imaginations of others, the more likely it is to be called beautiful by large numbers of people. The good news is that there is virtually no one or nothing that would not be perceived as beautiful by someone!

Perfume

For centuries, perfume making was chiefly an Oriental art. The Hebrews learned it from the Egyptians; there are frequent mentions of scent in the Bible particularly in Song of Solomon. In ancient civilizations of Egypt, Greece, Rome, and Asia perfumes figured everywhere. Taking their cue from the Egyptian culture, men in all of these civilizations rubbed scented oils on their beards, eyebrows, the soles of their feet, and, eventually, on handkerchiefs and stationery as well. Perfumes have been found in the tombs of the Egyptian pharaohs and, apparently, Egyptians even used perfumes to embalm their dead. It was a common practice in Rome to rub the palm of the hand with perfumed oils so that a handshake would transmit one's scent in the process. Romans, being masters and aficionados of the art of rhetorical public speaking,

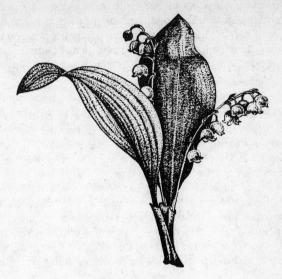

Lily of the Valley

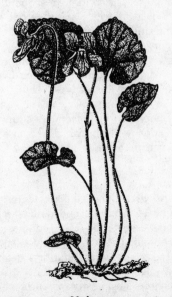

Violet

are credited with being the first to apply scent to the wrists so that the act of gesticulation would disseminate the perfume into the crowd. In the homes of royalty and the nobility incense burned incessantly and flowers littered the bedchambers. In fact, the word "perfume" is derived from the Latin words *per*, meaning "through," and *fumus*, meaning smoke.

History. Perfume traveled gradually from the East to the West. The crusaders helped bring perfume to the West during the thirteenth century. By the sixteenth century, perfumes were popular throughout Europe. During the Middle Ages, clothing was placed among bags scented in accordance with the season: in summer, roses, violets, and lilies were used; in winter, musk, aloe, and balsam. Sanitation conditions did not allow for frequent bathing. Most Westerners at this time considered the procedure unhealthy if indulged in more than once a month; therefore, the practice of (per)fumigating clothes was essential! Also, medieval men and women commonly believed that the use of perfume caused the blood to move through the veins more energetically and the skin to glow.

During the Renaissance, Queen Elizabeth I of England scented her gloves, shoes, and cloak daily. Reputedly, her favorite aroma was made from eight grams of musk, placed in eight spoonfuls of rosewater and a quarter of an ounce of sugar, which was then boiled for five hours and strained. Also during this period, dry sachets and perfumed lamps were crafted and sold by artisans.

In the extravagant French court of Versailles, noblewomen were expected to wear a different scent every day. Even during his military campaigns, Napoleon insisted on being well supplied with scented soaps and eau de cologne. One of the earliest American contributions to perfumery was manufactured during colonial times by Caswell-Massey Company, Ltd., which claims to be the "oldest chemists and perfumers in America"; their No. 6 Cologne is still available today.

Manufacturing Methods. Almost all perfumes manufactured today are created from a blend of synthetic and natural substances. Synthetic chemicals have been used extensively in perfumes since the nineteenth century and largely obtained from natural sources such as petrochemicals and coal tar. Essential oils are the substances extracted from plants and used by perfumers as the foundation of a scent. Oils extracted from rare flowers are found in the most costly perfumes. In the United States, many synthetic substances have been developed to meet the rising demand for perfumes, since many plants from which favorite essential oils are extracted are not native. However, many essential oils are imported in order to meet consumer demands.

Although most colognes and toilet waters are commonly referred to as perfumes, a "true perfume" is made with a higher concentration of extracted oil and is, therefore, more expensive. True perfumes contain 10 to 20 percent essential oil dissolved in alcohol, while colognes have only 3 to 5 percent oil dissolved in 80 to 90 percent alcohol, with water comprising the balance. Toilet waters have only 2 percent perfume oil in 60 to 80 percent alcohol and the balance is purified water.

Aside from essential oils and synthetic materials, perfumes contain animal substances that act as fixatives to slow the evaporation process. These include castor oil from the beaver, musk from the civet and the musk deer, and ambergris from the sperm whale.

Today many manufacturers make unscented cosmetics. The availability of unscented products allows the consumer to coordinate scents or ensure that a favorite perfume is relatively free from competition. Many cosmeticians design sets of perfume, powder, and lotion so that the modern man or woman need not be concerned with the task of coordinating scents.

Effects. Perfumes have profound physiological and psychological effects on human beings. Scent is also deeply entrenched in ritual religious practice. In ancient primitive cultures, resin, wood, and gum from pleasantly odorous plants were burned in ceremonies, and up until recently (and still during special services), during the course of mass, most Catholic churches would become enveloped in a cloud of the smoke from burning incense. Mohammed himself encouraged his followers to use perfumes.

However, even with the impressive advances in manufacturing technology, much of the mechanics that trigger human emotional responses to olfactory stimulation remain a mystery. Some smells release unconscious memories, stored up since childhood. Very little is known about the biological and chemical processes whereby humans distinguish one smell from another. In any case, it is universally recognized that the sense of smell is very powerfully entangled with human passions and behavior. Neurobiologists are even researching methods for improving working conditions by using appealing scents in the environment. Recognition of the power of an attractive scent is reflected in the fact that today, in the United States alone, perfume is a billion-dollar-per-year industry.

See also: AROMATHERAPY, ESSENCE, SENSE OF SMELL

How to Select a Scent

In choosing a scent, a traditional tendency has been to recommend floral scents for blondes and fair-complexioned women, and Oriental fragrances for darker skinned persons and brunettes. Most importantly, a fragrance should be chosen that pleases the user and that blends with, as opposed to dominates, the body's natural scent. Some perfumers claim that the integrity of the match between a person and a perfume is proven by whether or not it will linger throughout the day without frequent reapplication. Also, an individual should consider his or her age and force of personality when choosing a scent. Because we become acclimated to our own scent, it is important to be wary of the potential for excessive, and, therefore, offensive, application.

Permanent

The permanent has revolutionized the hair-care industry. In the early twentieth century, a semi-permanent waving process was introduced onto the market, although it was available only to the rich. Those women who could afford it now had at their disposal an elegant style that required relatively minimal maintenance. In 1906, Charles L. Nessler of London refined the process using a borax paste and electric heat and reportedly charged his customers a modest $1,000 per job. By 1915, manufacturers in the United States had improved the chemicals involved in the process and were able to reduce the price dramatically. During the thirties, the inexpensive, heat-free "cold wave" was developed, the process still employed today. Permanently waved hair, although it experienced a brief fall from favor during the sixties, remains a preferred option for many women. What was initially a twelve-hour, costly procedure is now, due to technological advances, a fairly simple, inexpensive two-hour affair.

See also: HAIR, HAIR MAINTENANCE

Personal Beautification

Entangled with the very evolution of the human species is the tradition of personal beautification. Anthropologists list bodily adornment among the behaviors belonging to every known culture in history. Human beings appear to be biologically programmed to strive toward greater personal attractiveness. "What is Beauty?" is as frequent a query among civilized persons as "What is the meaning of life?" Lower animals are also aware of beauty; for example, the bluebird constructs elaborately ornate nests to attract a mate, chimpanzees spend long hours grooming each other far beyond the demands of hygiene in acts of ritualistic bonding; but animals are largely compelled by instinct. Because humans have the ability to self-reflect, the pursuit and dissemination of beauty increase exponentially at the level of human culture.

Early Evidence. The concept of beauty can be traced to the beginning of culture. *Homo habilis* was an early ancestor of *Homo sapiens* who lived two million years ago. Anthropologists attribute to them the first rudimentary culture because of the red ochre paint found buried with their skeletons. Presumably this paint was used on the body for beautification as part of some kind of primitive ritual. The burial practices of the ancient Egyptian civilization also provide insight into their perception of the importance of beauty. The Egyptians elaborately painted the faces of the dead and covered them with precious jewels and elegant robes, indicating a belief that one's physicality remains valuable in the afterlife. They believed that beautiful enshroudment ensured that they might enter their next life in an appealing fashion, thereby gaining the gods' approval.

Health and beauty have long been associated with one another. Although the fourteenth century Italian lyric poet Petrarch claimed that "rarely do great beauty and great virtue dwell together," at least since the time of classical Greece, beauty has been closely aligned with goodness and has been viewed as a reflection of both spiritual and physical health. In primitive societies, the shaman, or medicine man, initially directed the process of self-adornment within a tribe. Body paint and ornamental accessories were worn in order to win favor with the gods in hopes of procuring relief from sickness.

Universal Criteria. Although beauty has consistently been a priority in virtually every civilization, notions of the beautiful ideal are far-ranging.

As Ralph Waldo Emerson stated, "One man's beauty [is] another's ugliness." David Hume, the Scottish philosopher, believed that there can be no universally acceptable standard of beauty. He said that standards are inevitably "relative, local and highly personal." Darwin believed that man's separation into such widely different races was the result of the multiplicity of differences in local aesthetic tastes. Is there, then, any universal aspect of ideal beauty? By moving away from definitions that are too specific, a few universal preferences can be identified. Youth and health do seem to be universal elements of the beautiful. This is not the result of repressed libido, as some Freudian analysts would claim, but instead reflects an instinctive biological concern with the survival of the species. This also explains why the vast majority of cultures throughout history have sought to stress the differences between the sexes in the art of personal adornment.

It is undeniable that humans everywhere are willing to make great sacrifices and endure tremendous pain in the name of beauty. The ideals toward which men and women strive can be identified in the artwork that a culture produces, particularly in representations of the human form. Throughout human history, an infinite number of poets, artists, philosophers, sociologists, and scholars have sought to encapsulate a definitive conception of beauty. The most common theme in poetry, song, and painting is the celebration of the beautiful beloved.

In addition to the relationship between beauty and creative inspiration, a particular connection between women and beauty pervades world cultures. This phenomenon is possibly due to the fact, as one philosopher speculates, that the curved line is considered more pleasant to the eye than the straight line, and women's shapes are more curved. Furthermore, physically beautiful persons are perceived as possessing the power of enchantment, a power chiefly reserved for women when other forms of conquest remained largely inaccessible. Recent evidence even suggests that parents spend more time with beautiful babies than with ugly babies, even though they are not willing to admit it.

How beauty is perceived and to what degree it is accepted remains a deep, unpredictable mystery. One significant sociological study has demonstrated that people themselves are perceived as more attractive when their surroundings are aesthetically pleasing. This reinforces the logic of carefully attending to that which surrounds the body most intimately, such as hair and clothing. In any case, artists, thinkers, and the average person will continue struggling to create—in words, stone, paint, and living flesh—more and better manifestations of beauty. As this common desire is recognized as a global phenomenon, local appreciation of beauty is likely to become more varied and complex.

pH Balance

pH, meaning potential hydrogen, is the scale used to determine the degree of acidity or alkalinity of a given solution. pH is not an ingredient and it is not a measure of gentleness or quality per se. The pH scale is from 0 to 14. The low end of the spectrum is the acid side and the top end is the alkaline side; the midpoint (7) is neutral. Pure water is a neutral substance. All cosmetics or solutions are either acidic or alkaline.

Many cosmetic products now boast having a "pH balance." This development marks an increased understanding of the importance of matching the acid-alkaline balance in cosmetic products with the natural acid-alkaline balance of regions of the body. The skin produces naturally a slightly acid mantle as a means of protection against bacteria. Soap is generally an alkaline product; unfortunately, it washes away this acid mantle along with dirt and grime. This is why it is wise to follow up washings with the application of an astringent (a skin freshener or toner) designed to restore the skin's natural pH balance. However, there are many soaps now manufactured which have a low pH. This means they are less likely to wash away the entire acid mantle of the skin.

The hair is also slightly acidic by nature. In addition to warding off microbes which cause infection, this acidity enables hair to retain moisture. Excessive use of alkaline products can be quite damaging to the hair, drying it out and making it brittle. Hair conditioners are designed to restore the acid to the hair in addition to making hair more manageable.

The natural, healthy pH of skin ranges from 4.5 to 5.5. Cosmetics or lotions with a higher pH can cause skin irritation. Cosmetic products which do not indicate their pH may be tested at home before applying them to the body. (Easy-to-use Nitrazine litmus paper is available at pharmacies.) Makeup should have a pH of 5, and skin care products such as lotions and moisturizers should have a pH of 4.5 to 5.5. Although the body's pH fluctuates, a skin pH of below 5 or above 6 indicates stress and physical disorders. Interestingly, as with many aspects of beauty, this proportion places the ideal in a slightly asymmetrical position between two ends of a scale. The Greeks identified a similar proportion in the natural world, known as the Golden Mean, which they cultivated in art. With the Golden Mean, a frame, a scale, a building, a sculpture, or human face is said to be most beautiful when the compositional elements are arranged to form two divisions along an axis so that the ratio of the two halves and the ratio of the larger half to the whole are both .618, i.e., slightly more than one half. Thus, it appears that beauty has a preferred location slightly off-center.

See also: ASTRINGENT, SOAP

Physiognomy

Physiognomy is the practice of classifying character traits by observing bodily, especially facial, features. Although many physiognomists disagree, some of the common determinations are that a high forehead is a sign of great intelligence and a receding chin is a mark of cowardice. This "science" overlooks the fact that facial features have meaning and beauty only in relationship to each other. Besides, there is no correlation between the features one is born with and the subsequent character that develops beneath those features.

Despite its shortcomings, the practice of physiognomy is ancient and widespread. Many ancient scholars, the pillars of Western culture including Plato, Aristotle, Aristophanes, Plutarch, Seneca, and Pythagoras, believed emphatically in physiognomy. The first printed text on physiognomy, written by an astrologer, dates back to 1272. Shakespeare makes frequent references to the facial features of his characters as a means for revealing personality traits. Popular interest in the subject persisted well into the eighteenth century.

In 1772, a theologian named Johann Kaspar Lavater published a book entitled *Essays on Physiognomy: Designed to Promote the Love of Mankind* that was an overnight success. It was quickly translated into several languages. Partially due to the quality of the illustrations, this work was reprinted in edition after edition for over a hundred years. The author's chief motive, as the title proclaims, was to encourage universal love among human beings and respect for the "work of God" as revealed in the face. But even in Lavater's exhaustive exploration of the subject, the major problem with physiognomy remains. It tends toward simplistic, metaphoric readings; for example, a straight nose is the mark of a straightforward, upright character. Also, Lavater's thesis cannot be reconciled with the natural history of and actual facts about human facial anatomy.

The most detrimental aspect of this pseudoscience is that it can and did lead many people to feel self-conscious or ashamed about imagined defects, features that were purely the result of genetic chance, not character flaws. The actions of Nazi Germany are a painful example of how such "knowledge" can be grossly misused. It manipulates the human desire for both self-improvement and quantifiable knowledge by providing quick, simplistic answers. Happily, no subject matter with human beings as its focus is that easy to categorize.

Pigment

Pigment is a coloring matter. The word is used to refer to both the substance in the cells and tissues of plants and animals that gives them color and the insoluble powder in paints, plastics, printing inks, and cosmetics. There are very few manufactured products that do not use or require products developed by the dyestuffs and pigment industry.

All dyestuffs and most pigments are complex organic compounds, mainly synthesized from coal tar or petrochemical products. The compounds rely on chemical structure for their color. The organic pigments are brighter and last longer because their chemical structure is less fragile. Synthetic organics include red, orange, yellow, and copper phthalocyanides, that is, the brilliant colors. Inorganic pigments are derived from earths: rocks, minerals, ceramics, enamels, and precious stones. They are generally combined with synthetics to derive a white opaque pigment used to lighten other pigments.

For centuries, humans used natural pigments extracted from plants, mollusks, and dried insects. Today most of the pigments used in cosmetics are synthetic. A few natural cosmetic lines produce makeup made with natural pigments—dried earth, ground safflowers, and an array of vegetable stuffs. However, these products are far more expensive and difficult to mass-produce.

Posture

"Beauty without grace is the hook without the bait."
—Ralph Waldo Emerson, *The Conduct of Life*

Posture is exceedingly important to general health and physical attractiveness. Good posture helps prevent fatigue, allows organs to function more efficiently, permits the voice a fuller range, endows a person with a look of confidence, and increases gracefulness. Regular exercise and conscious habit assist in forming good posture.

Correcting poor posture is a crucial step toward beauty on the inside as well as out. To a large degree, beauty is influenced by the grace, ease, and assertiveness with which a person moves. These characteristics are reflected in posture that is neither too stiff nor too lax. And, except in the case of deformity, good posture is simply a matter of self-discipline.

How to Maintain Good Posture

Examine the body carefully for drooping shoulders, an arched back, a perpetually dropped head, and a soft, projected abdomen. All of these posture problems can be rectified with the assistance of an inner voice articulating regular reminders.

The extent to which the spine is out of line, causing poor posture, can be determined in two ways. Sit with the back against a wall and try to press the entire length of the spine against it; or lie on a flat surface with the knees bent and soles of the feet on the floor and do the same. The push-up position is good for strengthening and straightening the spine of both men and women.

In occupations that involve standing a great deal, it is important to distribute weight evenly, concentrated on the balls as opposed to the heels of the feet. Do not lock the knees but keep them slightly flexed at all times. Strong stomach muscles lead to a strong lower back and, therefore, a straighter spine.

Pregnancy

The most dramatic changes possible in a human body occur during pregnancy. Inside the mother, a baby grows ten thousand times bigger within the first month alone! This is one of the most exhilarating and challenging periods in a woman's life.

Many feel that a woman's beauty often blossoms during pregnancy, but beauty during pregnancy is the result of concerted mental and physical attention to the body's needs. With the tremendous number of changes taking place within her, this is often the first time some women take serious note of their bodies.

Feeling positive about the way one looks during pregnancy is emblematic of excitement for the process as a whole. Many women feel ashamed of their increased bulk during pregnancy. However, numerous cultures have celebrated the shape of the pregnant women, even creating religious icons which glorify it and seek to capture its power. Most painters and sculptors have relished the aesthetic appeal of the pregnant form. Recently, our own culture is coming around, and the special beauty of a pregnant women is being acknowledged, for example in the variety of clothing available for pregnant women.

The first step to securing a sense of physical radiance is a matter of attitude and self-confidence. A healthy diet and exercise are deeply interconnected with this sense of confidence. The right combination will control weight gain, help maintain good circulation, keep energy up, increase flexibility and strength, and promote a faster recovery after delivery.

It is also important to pamper the body cosmetically. The skin is the mirror of all the changes taking place within the body. Commit to a simple complexion routine twice a day: cleanse the skin, then freshen with a toner or astringent, moisturize, and finally, protect it with a light foundation. Treat oneself to a facial mask once or twice a week. While bathing, scrub the entire body with a loofah sponge and the especially rough areas with a pumice stone. Then massage the body thoroughly with a moisturizing lotion. It is important to give extra care to one's enlarged breasts, which are particularly sensitive and susceptible during this time. (Cocoa butter is a good preventive against the development of stretch marks.) Also, invest in a good, supportive bra. Because estrogen and progesterone alter the pH balance in saliva, gums are more likely to bleed and teeth loosen; therefore, it is wise to visit the dentist twice during the term of one's pregnancy. Furthermore, the look of the hair, that feature so important to how one feels about the quality of one's physical appearance, is likely to change repeatedly. The best advice is to pay careful attention to these changes and change one's beauty regime in response. To complete the external celebration of creating a new life, give some thought to one's clothes. This does not mean spending exorbitant amounts of money; choose clothes that are comfortable, that accommodate your individual taste, and that complement your good points. Feeling attractive is likely to guarantee that you are perceived as such!

Pumice

Pumice is a spongy, light, highly porous volcanic rock long used in solid or powdered form to scour, smooth, and polish. This stone, which is the product of volcanic eruptions, is widely distributed over the earth's surface, particularly on the ocean floors. Although it is found underwater, when it is first loosened, it will float on the surface for months.

Cosmetically, pumice is used to remove hair, calluses, and stains from the skin. Regular use on the feet, hands, elbows, and knees will soften rough, hard skin. However, too much and too aggressive rubbing can irritate the skin. Always soak the area to which the pumice will be applied in soapy water first.

Pumice stones can be purchased at natural foods stores and toiletry shops.

Renaissance

The Renaissance, literally meaning "rebirth," was the period in Western history when classical learning was rediscovered and civilization began to modernize. It began in Italy in the fourteenth century, although its roots can be traced approximately to the eleventh century, and it lasted until about the sixteenth century.

Much of the literature and art of this period reveal information about the grooming practices of the time. One Italian philosopher described the most beautiful woman of that period as fair "fringed with rose" with bright blue eyes, plump, erect, and elegant, possessing thick lips, polished teeth, dimpled chin, ample bosom and "beautifully arranged toes." An influential Italian lawyer of the day, Fienzuola, wrote a treatise on beauty with exacting, precise demands for the ideal female beauty. His qualifications are so detailed as to require that the outside edge of a woman's ear should be "dusky red."

The elegant, soft beauty of Renaissance women was immortalized by such painters as Botticelli, Leonardo da Vinci, Raphael, Giorgione, and Titian. A pale complexion was an emblem of nobility for men and women, since tanned skin was associated with laborers who worked in the sun. Some women bleached their skin with a glaze made from egg white, tartar, lemon juice, and the sap of a birch tree. Meanwhile, Shakespeare, in his sonnets, was defending the appeal of swarthiness in the form of his "dark lady." Many women shaved their eyebrows and hairline to create the appearance of a more prominent forehead, said to be a mark of intelligence.

See also: ART AND IDEAL FEMININE BEAUTY

Rhinoplasty (Nose Surgery)

Rhinoplasty, or nose surgery—today known as a "nose job"—is the most frequently performed cosmetic surgical procedure across the globe.

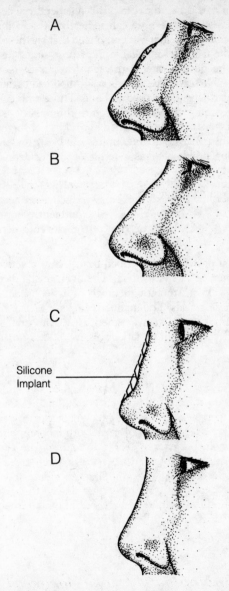

A

B

C

Silicone
Implant

D

Rhinoplasty. Drawing A shows where a hump will be removed. B shows the result after surgery. Figure C indicates where a silicone implant will be inserted under the skin. Figure D is the result after the implant.

The reason for this is twofold. First, it is a generally accepted fact that changing the shape of the nose can radically alter an individual's appearance. Leonardo da Vinci was convinced that the nose set the whole character of the face. Also, because most nose surgery is done within the nostrils, the nose is one of the few features that can be altered without noticeable scars. The nose is easily modified because it is largely composed of cartilage as opposed to bone. Those who consider surgery to correct a receding chin usually require rhinoplasty as well or their appearance may actually be worsened. This kind of surgery is not covered by most insurance companies unless it is being undertaken to remedy a breathing problem or as a result of an accident or congenital illness.

See also: COSMETIC SURGERY

Rome

The classical poet Ovid prescribed beauty care practices for Roman men and women in *Ars Armatoria*. The average standard of elegance was very high. The aristocratic members of society spent several hours a day on cosmetic rituals. The infamous emperor Nero, when he wasn't torturing Christians, used many cosmetics including chalk to whiten his complexion, Egyptian kohl to darken his eyes and lashes, and red fucus,

Saffron

obtained from rock lichen, on his lips and cheeks. He and other beauty-conscious Romans used ground pumice stone on the teeth to whiten them. However, this practice removed the enamel along with the stains!

Romans made imaginative use of what they found in their environment. Blush was made from wine dregs, eye shadow from powdered ash or saffron, and mascara from burnt cork. The Romans were especially fond of blond hair; hair bleaching was, therefore, quite common. Also, noble women and courtesans wore blond wigs made from hair brought back from conquered Gaul.

Rome, being a civilization obsessed with hygiene, perfected the cosmetic bathing ritual. After a bath, or a series of baths, the body was anointed with olive oil which had been mixed with crushed flowers. The Romans were also given to some peculiar practices of self-adornment; women gilded their nipples with gold dust, and men of fashion frizzed their hair then sprinkled it with gold dust. Nero's paramour, Poppoea, slept every night in a facial mask made from asses' milk, as she believed that it softened the skin.

See also: OVID

Roses

"Then glut thy sorrow on a morning rose."
—John Keats, "Ode on Melancholy"

"They that have roses
Never need bread."
—Dorothy Parker,
"There Was One"

As an emblem of beauty, the rose has occupied a prominent place in art, literature, medicine and, of course, horticulture for centuries. Greek writers made poetic reference to the rose as early as 600 B.C., and a replica of a rose is found on a Greek coin dated 325 B.C. Representations of the rose have been found in Egyptian art and architecture, and on Abyssian tombs from the first to fifth centuries A.D. (suggesting that roses were the official funereal offering). Cleopatra used the rose in ceremonial rites more frequently than the lotus blossom, although the latter is more often associated with the East. The rose garden of King Midas was one of the wonders of the ancient world.

The first example of European praise for the rose is found in a work dating back to the sixteenth century B.C. A golden-yellow rose with six petals is depicted in a Minoan fresco at Knossus, Crete. The rose retained its popularity during the Roman Empire, and the Romans were instrumental in the rose's widespread distribution. It is interesting to note that the only historical period in which roses were not valued highly as emblems of great beauty was during the time of intellectual stagnation following the fall of Rome. However, during the Dark Ages, roses were maintained in monastic gardens and the fruits, or hips, of the flowers were strung on rosaries; "rosary" itself means a wreath of roses.

In all cultures familiar with the flower, the word "rose" denotes not only a flower but also "red." The first roses were probably deep pink in color, from whence comes the genus name *Rosa*. Although Shakespeare's Juliet proclaims convincingly from her balcony that "a rose by any other name would smell as sweet," one might wish to qualify this eloquent assertion somewhat. In a successful marketing effort, the hybrid known as the Mme. Ferdinand Jamin was renamed the American Beauty rose and experienced a spectacular escalation in sales. Yet, over time, it is not its name but the transcendent quality of its beauty that accounts for the rose's popularity.

Mythology and Symbolism. Roses figure in both Eastern and Western myths. In Hindu religious mythology, Brahma and Vishnu—two of the three spirits attributed with the creation of the universe—argue over which flower is the most beautiful in the world. Brahma insists that it is the lotus blossom until Vishnu produces a rose for his inspection, whereupon Brahma concedes defeat.

For the ancient Greeks and Romans, the rose was associated with Aphrodite/Venus, the goddess of love. In mythology, the rose's origin is described as a result of Aphrodite's first tears or as a gift from the other gods when she first emerged from the sea. These stories also seek to explain the rose's red color. One version suggests that, as she was searching for her lost lover Adonis, she pricked her fingers on the thorns and her blood dyed the flowers red. Another attributes the color to her mischievous son, Cupid, who emptied a glass of red wine upon them. Cupid, in one tale, is also held accountable for the thorns: he was innocently smelling a lovely rose when a bee stung him; in his anger, he shot an arrow, missed the bee, and penetrated the bush. This myth shows the ancient association of the rose with romantic love. Due to its innately paradoxical nature, the rose has long been a favorite metaphor for poets and lovers. Like love, it intoxicates; it is a delicate blossom that can leave the careless pursuer bleeding from the jabs of unnoticed thorns. The origin of the rose, like love itself, is mysterious; fossil specimens indicate that it has been growing on the North American continent for at least thirty-two million years!

The rose, as a symbol, occupies a singular position in poetry. It has been used almost to the point of exhaustion, from whence comes the cynical, Modernist comment of Gertrude Stein, "A rose is a rose is a rose is a rose." But this place of metaphoric privilege is as old as the oral tradition, as heard in Homer's oft repeated invocation to "rosy-fingered Dawn" in *The Odyssey*. The meanings attributed to roses vary, sometimes in accordance with their color: the red rose speaks of passion; the white rose derives purity and chastity from its early association with Christian religious rituals; the yellow rose emblemizes drama and adventure; the pink rose symbolizes youthfulness and modesty. This last comes from a story about Eve who, in the Garden of Eden, kissed a white rose; it blushed and became forever pink. The blooming rose has also been associated with emerging knowledge as in Keats poem "The Eve of St. Agnes":

> *Sudden a thought came like a full-blown rose,*
> *Flushing his brow, and in his pained heart*
> *Made purple riot.*

However, the thread that weaves these meanings together is the sense of beauty which accompanies heartfelt, affirmative human sentiments.

Rose

The rose family is comprised of some two thousand species including trees, herbs, and shrubs. The rose is a remarkably hearty plant that grows easily in many parts of the world in diverse soils and climates. However, it does particularly well in temperate and mild zones. It has been very responsive to cultivation, and thousands of varieties have been developed through hybridization, the process of crossbreeding. Attar, the oil extracted from rose petals, is used in many perfumes and toilet waters. We now know that the fruit, or hip, of the rose contains a very high concentration of vitamin C.

The rose persists as a near-universal symbol of beauty as well as being the all-time favorite perennial flower. It is the flower that represents the month of June, a month typically associated with weddings and other celebrations of passage; it is the month that inaugurates many new creatures into the animal world as well. Within this one flower, which humans intuitively recognize as a significant representation of beauty, we witness the union of several crucial universal components of beauty: that which appeals to the senses of sight and smell, is healthy and healthful, and thrives in all sorts of cultures and climates.

Self-Mutilation

"Holes are bored through the lower part of the left nostril for the nose ring, and all around the edge of the ear for jewels. This may appear barbarous to the foreign eye; to us it is a beauty! Everything changes with the clime."
> —Anandubai Joslee, letter to Mrs. Carpenter (1880)
> quoted in *The Life of Anandubai Joslee*
> by Caroline H. Dull

By and large, self-mutilation is performed to conform with or perfect the aesthetic ideals of the culture. What one culture would define as self-mutilation another would simply consider the price for acquiring enviable beauty and a desirable place in society. In Africa, Sara women in Chad insert pieces of wood as large as plates in their lips in order to increase their size, and stretch their earlobes with weights. The Mangbelu of the Congo wear rings around their necks to stretch the length. Men and women in many African societies, such as the Bamileke, carve elaborate scars in their flesh to enhance their physical appeal and symbolize initiation and integration into the community. Indian women carve tiny holes in their forehead and insert jewels as ornamentation. Head deformation dates back to the pre-Neolithic epoch; it was practiced by Egyptian rulers, highborn Greek and Roman families, American Indians, and native Australians (or Aborigines). The Aborigine's passage through life is marked by self-induced alterations in teeth, skin, hair, and extremities. Samoan men are tattooed at puberty from the waist to the knees. Pretty girls sing to the men to keep their courage up because it is an extremely painful process that causes extensive blood loss. It is regarded as a compensation for the pain women endure during childbirth. Nineteenth century Spanish beauties would sleep all night with their hands tied up by pulleys in order to make them bloodless and white. The excruciating process of binding women's feet was practiced by the Chinese for nearly one thousand years. Even though it resulted in deformity and crippled women so that they could barely move without assistance, it was considered exceedingly attractive. Courtesans in ancient Rome and highborn Moslem women (even today) plucked their pubic hair. Men and women in the West spend vast sums annually to alter their nose, face, ears, breasts, and hairline.

Many practices of self-mutilation are associated with spiritual matters. In *The Golden Bough*, J. G. Frazer lists over fifty examples of cultures that perform some form of self-mutilation in times of mourning. Self-flagellation was common among devotees of the Catholic faith. The Aztecs let blood, cut their ears, and perforated their tongues in hopes of pleasing the gods.

While all of these practices may strike the visitor from an alien culture as peculiar, it is undeniable that humans everywhere are willing to make great sacrifices and endure tremendous pain to live up to the standards established by their culture. This stems from the fact that ethics and aesthetics are intertwined in the minds of most humans; therefore, what is perceived as good behavior from an ethical standpoint acquires an air of beauty, and vice versa.

The question remains: why are people willing, even eager, to go to such lengths for personal adornment? A probable answer to this question is crystallized in the attitude toward the body of most black African civilizations. For them, the human body is the object of mythic interpretation. The Dogon perceive each individual body as a microcosm of the entire world—the world which emerged from the primordial egg just as each human being emerges from an egglike casing, the womb. From religious expression it is a short step to aesthetic expression. Historically, body decoration for special feast days led shortly to artistic elaborations for the sheer pleasure of creating more beauty for its own sake. The body was, and remains, the chief focus of artistic expression in most African tribes. It is altered in the course of integrating the individual into society, struggling to make sense out of life, and as an attempt to ward off sickness and danger.

Manipulation of the body is a means for socialization, philosophizing, and achieving physical and spiritual health. Anthropologists also associate these three motivations with the human impulse to create art. The body, for the would-be sculptor—in other words, every individual in every culture—is the first and most tangible clay. Scarification and tattooing are among the more obvious examples of "the body as a work of art," but some manifestation of this undertaking is displayed by every healthy individual. Self-mutilation, as long as it is practiced within the socially acceptable parameters of a given culture, must be understood as a symbol, an outward expression of the human desire to improve, to understand, and to survive.

Sense of Smell

The sense of smell is the most sensitive system in the human body as well as one of the most efficient. It is remarkably precise, although not nearly as precise as a dog's, which is over a million times more sensitive. Still, the average person is capable of identifying thousands of different scents, although the act of describing any specific scent in words is extremely difficult. Likewise, scientists' attempts to explain and categorize the mechanisms of the olfactory system that governs the sense of smell are somewhat feeble. The ability to smell is carried out by microscopically small organs, receptor cells with long hairlike structures called cilia embedded inside a mucus layer of the cells. Odors enter the nose as miniscule droplets which must be soluble in the mucus in order to be detected. These impulses are then chemically transferred to the brain.

Ancient cultures such as those of Egypt and Greece were acutely aware of the fact that body odors and perfumes trigger emotional responses. Modern science has confirmed this mysterious phenomenon, asserting that unpleasant odors can actually cause a person to feel physically ill, and pleasant odors can raise one's spirits and energy level. Also, it is uncontested, although unexplained, that scents have the power to elicit emotional memory recall.

Different smells combine to produce different, and sometimes even conflicting, sensations. The scent of most perfumes, for example, is quite complicated. While a perfume may smell wonderful in the bottle, it can smell radically different when applied to the bodies of different individuals; it alters as it combines with an individual's unique scent. Therefore, it is important to sample perfume on the skin before committing to any particular scent. The science of aromatherapy, which attempts to understand scents in relation to one another, is making new contributions to health and beauty care. Most notably, aromatherapy has played a part in developing new cosmetic products with organic ingredients.

To some extent, the degree to which a person finds another attractive is determined by how one responds to that person's natural odor. This unique odor can never be fully masked. Therefore, the best perfumes or colognes blend with and complement an individual's personal scent and do not attempt to overpower it. The "chemistry" between people certainly has something to do with a harmonious blend of scents. A study of olfactory characteristics along gender lines demonstrates that by smelling a tube of exhaled breath, 95 percent of both the men and women tested could accurately determine the sex of the donor. Also, each sex found it consistently easier to identify the breath of the opposite sex.

See also: AROMATHERAPY, ESSENCE, PERFUME

Seventeenth Century

As the Puritan movement in England took hold in the seventeenth century, cosmetics became associated with two groups of social outcasts: actors and prostitutes. The Puritans associated cosmetics with base vanity and sexuality, the influence of the devil, and the evils of the aristocracy. After the Puritans took over Parliament in England and the monarch Charles I was executed, they passed a law to prohibit "false" adornment. It read as follows:

All women, of whatever age, rank, profession or degree, whether virgins, maids, or widows, that shall from and after such Act, impose upon, seduce, and betray into matrimony, any of his majesty's subjects, by the scents, powders, cosmetics, washes, artificial teeth, false hair, Spanish wool, iron stays, hoops, high-heeled shoes and bolstered hips shall incur the penalty of the law in force against witchcraft and like misdemeanors and that the marriage, upon conviction, shall stand null and void.

Puritan legal restrictions enacted in colonial America prevented widespread use of cosmetics among the lower classes, youth, and indentured servants. But for all of this energy exerted, the Puritan political influence never managed to suppress the practice of personal beautification entirely. It remained a basic need, although it was performed more surreptitiously.

Shaman

A crucial member of the community in a multitude of primitive cultures is the shaman, the ecstatic figure who heals and communicates with the other world. "Shaman," derived from a Mongolian word, literally means "one who knows." In these cultures, illness is thought to be caused by loss of the soul, which has either escaped or been stolen by demons. The shaman, as interlocutor between the worlds of humans and the gods, plays the roles of medicine man, spiritual leader, village psychologist, aesthete, and chief performer. The shamanic figure exists in such widely diverse cultures as those of the Maoris, Polynesians, Mongolians, Eskimos, and the American Indians.

In shamanic ritual, the relationship between health and beauty is clearly discernible. In primitive societies, the shaman directs the process of self-adornment within a tribe. Body paint and ornamental accessories are worn in order to win favor with the gods in hopes of procuring relief from sickness. Most designs were painted on the body in red in patterns designed to "seduce" the healing spirit into the sick body.

See also: BODY PAINTING

Shampoo

Clean hair is an essential part of beauty, affecting both a person's skin and mood. A typical eighteenth century shampoo was made of oatmeal and egg, but most active persons living in today's world are more likely to clean the hair thoroughly with the aid of a commercial shampoo. Never use detergents or body soaps as a substitute; they damage the hair even as they clean. Most hair products are specially formulated to treat the specific structure of hair. Most shampoos are 25 percent soap and 50 percent water and oils. A beneficial shampoo should have a pH balance between 4.0 and 5.5.

It is wise to alternate between several different shampoos on a regular basis. Hair becomes acclimated to one formula and will respond less well over time. Before washing, brush hair and then soak it completely. Use water at the coolest possible temperature. Massage shampoo into the scalp. Be careful not to use too much; shampoo that is not rinsed thoroughly leaves a filmy, buildup on the hair, making it appear dull and lifeless. Follow shampoo with a conditioner to enhance the hair's body and repair heat damage.

See also: CONDITIONERS, HAIR, pH BALANCE

Shaving

Shaving the natural growth of body hair is, like most beautification practices, a mark of an evolving civilization. Archaeologists have discovered razors among the relics of the Bronze Age. Legend has it that Alexander the Great insisted that his army shave their beards as a defensive strategy (to prevent the enemy from having something to pull on), and shaving has been a traditional emblem of discipline in the military. However, among many early civilizations, beards as well as long hair were important signs of masculinity. The ancient association of beardlessness with the powerlessness of slaves and infants may have a great deal to do with the practice of shaving by women. This also explains why many feminists in the early seventies chose to forego shaving as a mark of rebellion and liberation. However, even the feminist writer Susan Brownmiller acknowledges the aesthetic appeal or smooth skin (*Femininity*, Linden Press, 1984). Smooth skin allows for a smoother line, which many considered to be more aesthetically pure; this is why ballet dancers of both sexes often shave their entire bodies. Again, the individual is confronted with the choice between a desired look and the sacrifice of time and energy it requires to maintain.

See also: HAIR

How to Get the Best Shave

Shaving is a delicate ritual. A shave should begin with a thorough cleaning of the skin. Apply lukewarm water and then shaving cream, gel, or soap. Teflon- or platinum-coated blades give the smoothest shave. Always shave in the direction of natural hair growth. Continually rinse the blade with hot water while shaving. Do not exert too much pressure; this impulse is usually prompted by a dull razor. After shaving, rinse the skin and pat it dry. Finally, if shaving the face, spray a light mist of purified water on it and seal with a moisturizer; finish off with an aftershave cologne. After shaving the legs, massage them thoroughly with a moisturizer—and be sure to include the feet in this final step.

Silicone

Silicone is a chemical compound containing a basic structure of alternate silicon and oxygen atoms and characterized by relatively high resistance to water and heat. It is used in creams, lotions, and nail polishes. Silicone may also be injected under the skin to change body shape, e.g., the size of the lips, the nose, etc. It is now illegal in the United States, however, to administer silicone injections to increase the size of breasts because of the high incidence of inflammations and infections. However, plastic surgeons still use silicone to remove the fine lines around the mouth by injecting it into the flesh above the upper lip.

See also: COSMETIC SURGERY, MAMMOPLASTY

Skin

"I'm tired of all this nonsense about beauty being only skin deep. That's deep enough. What do you want—an adorable pancreas?"

—Jean Kerr from "Mirror, Mirror on the Wall," in *The Snake Has All the Good Lines*

The skin is the boundary and contact between the body and the rest of the world. It is also a mirror of emotions; it blushes as an indication of embarrassment, pales with fear, and reddens with anger. As the outer covering for the human body, it serves two chief functions. It works as a protective screen against heat, cold, and the entrance of bacteria and chemicals. The skin is also a gateway into the body, receiving and transmitting moisture and tactile sensations. It is classified as an organ, the largest in the human body. If the skin of a 125-pound woman were stretched out flat it would cover a surface measuring approximately seventeen square feet.

Composition. The skin is made of three layers:

Epidermis—the outermost and thinnest layer, consists of four layers of cells. The surface layer of cells, called the horny layer, is made of rows of dying cells that are filled with the protein keratin, a substance that toughens the skin and that is also found in nails and hair. Keratin is used as an ingredient in many lotions and moisturizers because it is waterproof. Only the third, or basal, layer of the epidermis is composed of living cells. These cells, called keratinocytes, divide continually and produce melanin, a brown pigment, the amount of which determines skin color. As keratinocytes move toward the surface of the epidermis, they die and are eventually shed as fine flakes.

Dermis—the middle layer of the skin contains blood vessels that nourish the outer layers of the skin, nerve endings that enable the sense of touch and are situated in papilla (tiny points of elevation on the skin that help connect the three layers), and connective tissue.

Subcutaneous tissue—the thickest and deepest layer of the skin contains sweat gland ducts that release sweat when the body becomes overheated, thus helping to maintain a normal, healthy internal temperature. This layer also contains the erector muscles of hairs, hair follicles, papillae, connective tissues, blood vessels, and fat storage cells. This layer expands when excess body fat is produced. The thickness of this layer varies greatly from individual to individual. However, the normal body fat content as a subset of total body weight is 25 percent for adult women and 15 percent for men. The fat stored in the subcutaneous layer serves as an energy source for the body and is broken down as needed. The other chief functions of this skin layer are to retain heat and to absorb blows inflicted on the body.

Skin Types. Although cosmeticians classify skin as dry, normal, or oily, the category of normal is something of a misnomer. Only 20 percent of adults possess what is meant by normal skin; the vast majority have a combination of dry and oily patches on different areas of the skin. The

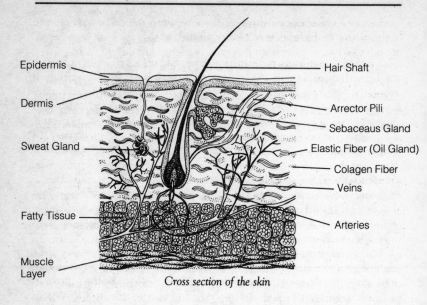

Epidermis

Dermis

Sweat Gland

Fatty Tissue

Muscle Layer

Hair Shaft

Arrector Pili

Sebaceaus Gland

Elastic Fiber (Oil Gland)

Colagen Fiber

Veins

Arteries

Cross section of the skin

average person tends toward more patches of dry skin after the age of twenty-five, as a lifetime of exposure begins to take its toll. It is important to determine skin type, localize specific problems, and acquire different products to meet the needs of each region. Applying greasy creams to oily patches or astringents to dry ones is counterproductive. The acquisition of beautiful skin begins with an intimate knowledge of the utterly unique layout of one's face.

Sun Damage. The sun is easily the greatest enemy of the skin. Although the body requires some exposure to sunlight to produce sufficient vitamin D (which is essential for the deposition of calcium and phosphorous in teeth and bones) excessive exposure damages the skin. Persons dwelling in harsher climates should take extra precautions to maintain the level of moisture in the skin. After sunbathing, moisturizers are crucial to restore depleted moisture. Also, during extended exposure to the sun, perfumes and other scented products not especially formulated to act as a sunscreen should be avoided; such products cause photosensitivity in some individuals and may result in irregular dark or light pigmentation. The valuable ingredients to look for in skin care products include aloe vera (that also functions as a natural sunscreen), lanolin, glycerine, silicones (that act as lubricants and emollients), and lipids (complex cell stimulators that produce new elastin, the basic constituent of elastic tissue). Tretinoin, a synthetic derivative of vitamin A, currently a component of some antiacne drugs, is being tested for its ability to reverse some of the visible effects of photodamaged skin.

Skin Care. Cleanliness, moisturizing, and good circulation are necessary for a healthy complexion. It is important to clean the skin thoroughly and regularly. The best soaps for cleansing the skin without drying it out are mild, low-detergent, nonalkaline, naturally scented products. Although any application of cleansers does inevitably dry the skin to some degree, cleansers are necessary as a part of hygiene and as an acne preventive. This is why cleansing and the regular application of lubricants and moisturizers should go hand in hand. Frequent stimulation of the skin through massage promotes circulation of the blood, giving skin a healthy sheen. In part, the regenerative potency of facials is a function of the fact that the process stimulates the flow of blood to the face, heightening natural coloring. Facial masks, now available at relatively low cost, can be purchased in cosmetic departments and health and beauty supply stores.

The application of cosmetics can actually be beneficial if products are chosen to suit one's skin type and particular needs. The application of base makeup in circular strokes stimulates the skin surface and provides a protective layer for the retention of moisture. However, cosmetics should always be removed thoroughly at the end of the day with moisturizing creams to prevent the accumulation of bacteria on the skin.

Moisturizers protect the skin against wind, sun, air-conditioning, central heating, and pollution. All of these environmental factors contribute to the speed with which skin ages. As the body ages, the skin grows thinner and dries out more easily. The fatty tissue that supports the skin becomes thinner. The visible indications of this aging process are wrinkles and scaliness. Therefore, the regular use of moisturizers becomes even more essential as time passes. The aging process cannot be escaped entirely, but because the skin is a regenerative organ that continually replaces itself, attentive care can extend the number of apparently youthful years an individual enjoys.

See also: ACNE, FACIALS

Sleep

> *"Our foster nurse of nature is repose."*
> —William Shakespeare

Sleep allows the body, particularly the communication network known as the central nervous system, time to rejuvenate itself. This does not mean that the body can (or should) shut down during sleep. Sleep is especially important for infants because it is during sleep that their bodies grow. Nutrients that help new skin cells form are not properly assimilated without sleep. Oxygen is brought into the body most efficiently during sleep. The body does not even need to remain very still for this to happen: in order to prevent muscle spasms, a person actually makes over 140 movements during eight hours of sleep. The entire body, including the mind, continue to work, but at a reduced pace. Some psychologists believe that dreams are actually "bait" to keep the brain interested long enough for the remainder of the body to rest. Dreams occur in hundred-minute intervals, in three to five different spurts during eight hours of sleep even though most people can only remember one short dream, if any, per night.

People deprived of sleep become sluggish, mentally unfocused, and short-tempered. Those who go without sleep for three days or more begin to have difficulty with sensory perception and are likely to have hallucinations. Though details about the nature of sleep remain a mystery to scientists, it is easy to recognize sleeplessness on the face and body of an individual. Dark circles under the eyes, sluggishness, slumping posture, pale complexion, and trembling hands are some characteristics.

The best position for sleeping is on the back with one leg slightly bent; the former allows for greater lung capacity and, therefore, deeper breathing, and the latter relieves strain from the pelvic area. Lying on the back also prevents pressure on various organs and the face. Sleeping on the stomach can actually contort the bone structure of the face and stretch the skin disadvantageously. Sleep with only one small pillow; big pillows inhibit full breathing and constrict the neck.

The average person usually falls asleep within fifteen minutes of lying down. Persons who have trouble sleeping should practice deep breathing exercises while consciously relaxing each part of the body, slowly moving the attention up from the toes to the top of the head. Calcium (found in dairy products) promotes undisturbed sleep and relaxes the muscles. Muscle spasms in the night can be an indication of a calcium deficiency. Eight hours of continuous sleep per night is considered the necessary norm for most persons. Some, however, only need six, while others require as much as ten. "Beauty sleep" is more than a whimsical expression; sufficient sleep is an essential component for maintaining physical and mental attractiveness.

"Sleeping Beauty"

Most modern children (young and old) know the story of how a beautiful princess, as the result of a wicked fairy's curse, falls into a comatose sleep on her sixteenth birthday after pricking her finger on the spindle of a spinning wheel; this sleep lasts for a hundred years and is ended at last by the kiss of a gallant prince who happens by at just the right moment. However, this version is quite different from the one first written down in Italy by Giambattista Basile in 1636. Renderings of this story date back to the fourteenth century, but in Basile's version, the prince does far more than kiss the sleeping princess; nine months later she gives birth to twins, a boy and a girl named Sun and Moon—and all that while she remains asleep! She awakens only after the baby boy, who has been sucking on her finger, dislodges the splinter that had inaugurated the sleep.

One day, the prince, remembering his adventure, returns, finds the princess awake, and admits to having sired the children. However, he leaves again to return to his wife. The wife, having somehow learned of the children's existence, has them brought to the palace and orders her cook to use them in preparing the evening meal. A stew is served and, afterwards, the wife announces to the prince that he has just eaten his illegitimate children. Meanwhile, the wife has also arranged to have the princess burned at the stake. The prince finally shakes off his lethargy and rescues her. The cook then reveals that she had actually substituted kid (as in goat) for kids; the children are still alive. The wife is put to death and the new family lives happily ever after.

At first, the connections between this tale and the more refined rendition passed down through the brothers Grimm may seem difficult to detect. However, both involve the necessity of doing away with the evil principle—be it a wicked fairy or a madly jealous wife—before goodness, via a harmonious, conjugal union, can flourish. But more important, it is the maturation of the teen beauty herself which is the central focus of the story.

At age sixteen she is "cursed" with a deep sleep. This hundred-year-long nap symbolizes a crucial phase in the psychological and physical flowering experienced by all young women. The maturing young woman undergoes a long period of self-absorption, generally during adolescence. During this time, her mind as well as her glands are so preoccupied with changes that she often appears physically exhausted. This external passivity and listlessness may seem to last an eternity (one hundred years), yet it is essential for her full development. Just as a rose most lie dormant during the winter in order to blossom, a teenager needs to retreat inward to ensure the healthiest conceivable coming of age.

Equally implicit in the story is the wisdom that having to wait awhile for sexual consummation does not detract from the beauty of romantically charged sex, but in fact, enhances it. Both mind and body must be sufficiently prepared, otherwise sex is experienced as a violation or "loss," not as a natural part of genuine, loving adult intimacy. "Sleeping together" should only happen after one has fully awakened!

In the story, the sleep comes to an end, just as childhood must. The fairy tale doesn't represent this as a tragedy—perpetual youth certainly would not be very interesting if it meant sleeping forever! The young beauty must eventually come to terms with the external world. In the latter-day version of this fairy tale the rest of the world, which has also been asleep, awakens along with the beauty herself. This addition to the story suggests how the girl's sensitivity to humanity in general can (and should) return after temporary immersion in a self-centered dream state. After attending to one's own needs, it is time to share that carefully nurtured beauty with the world.

As with all things in a temporal world, youthful beauty is subject to decay. Growing older is the necessary price of living in the world. But, as the story with its happily-ever-after ending suggests, this is not simply a lamentable fact of life; for beauty is frigid that remains static. The truly beautiful woman is she who changes gracefully through and with time. Attaining beauty, just like coming of age, is more than a physical process. It is the work of an entire lifetime.

Soap

Soap is a water-dispersible salt derived from a fatty acid. In ancient Sumeria, soap was made from vegetable extracts and oils. It was used solely for medicinal purposes; regular bathing was done with soda instead of soap. Soap was not recognized as a cleansing agent until the second century A.D. The Romans made soap from animal fats and wood ashes. Wood ashes contain potassium carbonate, an alkali; alkalies neutralize acids and break up soil because they are readily soluble in water. The production of soap nearly ceased during the Middle Ages because the Catholic church discouraged exposure of the flesh even to the point of frowning upon bathing. The manufacture of soap did not become an industry until the Leblance process of producing soda ash from brine was introduced in 1790. In the nineteenth century, an American traveling salesman named B. T. Babbitt was the first to make soap in a uniform size. He also imprinted his name on the surface of the soap bars so that his customers would have a continuous reminder of its origin. The first scents which were popular in bathing soap were musk and coal tar. In 1878, Harley Procter and James Gamble created the first delicate, subtly scented soap which they dubbed "White Soap." A factory accident which caused more then the required amount of air to be pumped into the product lead to the formation of the first floating soap. In order to capitalize on this new quality of airy buoyancy, "White Soap" was quickly renamed "Ivory" to emphasize its purity and a legendary marketing campaign ensued; the slogan for this soap was "so pure it floats."

Modern soap has a wide-ranging identity. Basically, soap is now made by direct hydrolysis of fats by water at high temperatures. The fats most commonly used are coconut oil and tallow. This process provides a denser concentration of the solvent glycerine. Good toilet soaps should be virtually exempt of free alkali. A pH value of more than 9.5 roughens the skin; the lower the pH, the milder the soap. Deodorant soaps contain antibacterial ingredients to fight surface bacteria produced by perspiration. Liquid soaps, distributed in plastic dispensers and tubes, are now quite popular. They are less messy and more easily conserved than bar soap. Cosmetic manufacturers have developed special complexion soaps to combat a wide variety of skin problems and to meet the specific needs of different skin types.

See also: DEODORANTS, pH BALANCE

Solvents

Solvents are liquids, chiefly water and alcohol, in which solid substances are dissolved. This is why purified water is a major ingredient in most cosmetics. Other compounds that are valuable as solvents because they break up substances that are insoluble in water include acetone, benzine, carbon disulfide, carbon tetrachloride, chloroform, and ether. Most solvents are organic compounds.

Spas

The objective of a visit to a spa, whatever its particular offerings may be, is the enhancement of personal health and beauty. The first major beauty spas (sometimes called beauty "farms") were constructed by the Romans. Although they were referred to simply as "the baths," they consisted of far more than bathing facilities and included everything from landscaped gardens to exercise rooms to libraries and stage areas for poetry readings. This was a place for total rejuvenation. The ancient civilizations of Greece, Japan, and China developed such beauty centers as well.

After several centuries in the West during which bathing of any sort was considered taboo and physical fitness and nutrition unheard of, the beauty spa gradually returned in a new and ever-improving version. In a town called Spau in what is now Belgium, fresh mineral springs discovered to have rejuvenating qualities became the center for a resort. This resort at Spau (which later became "Spa") provided the generic name for areas with mineral waters where people would come to "cure" ailments, reduce stress and fatigue, and generally revitalize themselves. The mud by-products from these regions were used in cosmetic masks and therapeutic baths. In the eighteenth and nineteenth centuries, the concerns of the spa manager expanded. The beauty of the landscape became an essential factor in determining a spa's merit. The spa as a center of aesthetic culture as well as aesthetic bodies gradually returned.

Modern beauty spas concentrate on weight loss, physical fitness, imparting nutritional awareness, and eliminating stress by pampering the body—both inside and out. A visit to a beauty spa is designed to be a productive holiday, a break in the pace of an individual's life. Some spas even offer counseling and follow-up programs so that the experience is more than a temporary respite from a manic, unhealthy life-style.

A visit to a spa can benefit anyone. Today, many doctors send hypochondriacs as well as genuine invalids to beauty farms as part of their general therapy. But even a healthy individual can experience marked improvements in energy level and the condition of the skin after a stay at a beauty spa. People with serious weight problems can enroll in special physician-directed programs which guard against injury and offer extra motivational support.

The most elaborate and elegant spas are located in France and Italy where the relationship between beauty, physical health, and pleasure has long been understood. American spas tend to emphasize fitness programs. Some beauty spas have even expanded their agendas to include drug abuse programs.

Stockings

The word "stocking" appeared in the English vocabulary during the sixteenth century, but the garment as we know it today took many years to work its way up the leg. The origins of both the word and the fashion item date back to about 600 B.C. in ancient Greece. *Sykhos* were a soft, form-fitting sandallike shoe that covered the toes and the heel and were worn exclusively by women. (Men who wore them were considered shamefully effeminate although actors donned them for comic gags.)

In northern Europe where weather conditions were a bit cooler, Germanic tribes wore loose trousers, called *heuse* that were lashed onto the legs with rope in a crisscrossing pattern. The men of Julius Caesar's legions protected their legs in a similar fashion with *hosa*.

Although logic should have it that a marriage between the ankle-high *sykhos* or *soc* and the leg-length *hosa* resulted in the modern stocking, this was not exactly the case. Stockings developed from the Roman *udones*. These were a sock made of goat's hair cloth which was said to soothe tired feet. When men wore *udones* without boots it was considered a mark of effeminacy.

By the fourth century A.D., thigh-high white stockings were a part of a priest's liturgical costume. Around the Continent, "skin tights" grew gradually more popular; in 1066, William the Conqueror introduced them to the British Isles. By the fourteenth century, the revealing, form-fitting character of stockings had become an emblem of the rebellious youth. The men the court of Henry VIII proudly displayed a well-formed calf through gold-embroidered stockings sewn onto their knee breeches. But in the late eighteenth century, with the quest for greater simplicity in dress, men began to put away all but their white silk stockings.

Women did not begin to wear stockings until the seventh century A.D. However, because of their long gowns and the general restrictions placed on feminine sensuality for centuries, there is little evidence in paintings, illustrations, or literature that women even had legs! But we do know that Chaucer's Wife of Bath wore stockings "of fine skarlet redde." By the sixteenth century during Queen Elizabeth's reign, women were wearing quite elaborate brightly colored and embroidered stockings, just as the men were, even though these were concealed under their long gowns.

In 1589, also during Elizabeth's reign, Reverend William Lee invented the "loome" for knitting stockings. This was the beginning of the modern hosiery industry. By the nineteenth century, women were the only ones wearing stockings: black lisle thread by day and silk by night.

In October 1938, the Dupont chemical company announced the advent of a new synthetic material called "nylon," a polyamide derived from carbon, oxygen, and hydrogen. This was both good and bad news for the undergarment business. On one hand, it meant liberation from fluctuations in the silk market; on the other, manufacturers feared this inexpensive and "indestructible" fabric would itself destroy the market altogether.

Although "nylons" were displayed at the 1939 World's Fair, Dupont did not allow their distribution until May 15, 1940, what the company dubbed international "Nylon Day." Apparently, no consumer item in history has ever created such hysteria. Departments were flooded with eager women and several near-riots broke out in fights over the limited supply. The demand persisted even though nylons vanished for a time during the forties because of the war. During this time, women made do with socks or a mock seam drawn down the back of the legs with an eyebrow pencil. The fact that a pair of nylon stockings was one of the most coveted black market items indicated the kind of future in store for this consumer product. (One indication of their significance today is the fact that the word "nylons" is used to refer only to female hosiery although nylon is found in a wide range of products.) Before long, silk stockings were virtually obsolete even though nylons soon proved to be far from "indestructible."

In the sixties with the introduction of the miniskirt, tights—the male garment of the fifteenth and sixteenth centuries—resurfaced. The manufacturers of nylons responded by changing the style in which hose were made to allow for greater visibility without unsightly lines. Now that it is thoroughly acceptable for a woman to display her legs, tights, nylon hose, and silk stockings of every imaginable variety, color, and texture fill the marketplace.

Stretch Marks

Stretch marks, medically termed striae, are breaks in the elastic fiber of the skin. The chain of causality begins with overeating or pregnancy, leading to excess fatty tissue. The key is that the change in body shape is relatively sudden rather than gradual. Certain medical conditions and synthetic steroids (like prednisone which is often prescribed for asthma) may also cause striae. Unfortunately, stretch marks cannot be removed, but they do, in some cases, fade over time. Scrubbing the skin regularly and gently with a loofah sponge helps soften the skin and deemphasize stretch marks. Wheat-germ oil, applied to the skin, works as a preventive.

Sunburn

Sunburn speeds the death of skin cells through dehydration of the dermis below the skin's surface. Immediately, it results in the rapid loss of the upper layer of skin through peeling. The long-range effects of sunburn include a loss of elasticity and resiliency, which causes premature wrinkles and even skin cancer.

Tanning is the body's self-defense against exposure to the sun. The production of melanin, brown skin pigment, is a natural sunscreen. However, a tan only provides a minimal screen against ultraviolet rays. Sunbathers should continue to wear sunscreen or sun block even after the skin has tanned. Persons living in harsh climates should invest in cosmetics with built-in sunscreens. A sunburn can also produce unsightly and painful mouth sores. Therefore, the lips, an especially sensitive region of the body, should always be protected from the sun with lipstick, balm, or sun block.

See also: SKIN, TANNING

Symmetry

> "It is more important to have beauty in one's equations than to have them fit the experiment . . . because the discrepancy may be due to minor features that are not properly taken into account and that will get cleared up with further developments of the theory. . . . It seems that if one is working from the point of view of getting beauty in one's equations, and if one has a really sound insight, one is on a sure line of progress."
>   —Paul Dirac,
>   "The Evolution of the Physicist's Picture of Nature,"
>   (*Scientific American*, May 1963)

Symmetry, generally speaking, is a perfect balance between two sides of an object. The term is applied to subjects of scrutiny in the arts and sciences. All researchers working in the fine arts recognize, however, that genuine symmetry creates a monotonous effect. In the pursuit of formulas for the beautiful ideal, broken symmetry is a recurrent theme scholars have detected in the art of both primitive and developed cultures. Broken symmetry implies a slight disruption of seemingly symmetrical design. Examples of this phenomenon are found in the face painting created by the Caduveo women of South America, in the Maori "moko" tattoos, the art of the ancient Chinese, classical Greek architecture, the art of North American Indians (past and present) and the graphic works of Dutch artist M. C. Escher.

All human faces are slightly asymmetrical. As Francis Bacon pointed out in the late sixteenth century, "There is no excellent beauty that hath not some strangeness in the proportion." This fact is easily apparent if one covers half of the face at a time and views in a mirror each half in immediate succession. Ancient folklore explained this phenomenon in pseudogenetic terms—the left half was obtained from the mother and the right from the father. One early scientist even propagated the theory that the conscious personality, or "true" face could be constructed from two left halves, while a double-right portrait was an expression of the darker, unconscious portion of an individual. More likely, the face is just another example of the broken symmetry that recurs throughout nature.

Cosmologist Paul Davies writes about the implications that current findings in cosmic physics will have for the way we perceive science, theology, and psychology in the future. He explains that broken symmetry is a fundamental element of the evolution of the universe. Each stage of the universe's history, the creation of more and more complex entities, has been caused by a breaking of the symmetry of simpler states. Symmetry breaking seems to be part of the innate software of the universe. One accessible example of this pattern is an embryo developing in the womb. Symmetry is repeatedly broken, beginning with a single DNA molecule, gradually producing an intricate pattern that ends up as a human being. Some scholars speculate that this general pattern—structures with broken symmetry—recurs because it has powerful survival value. The fact that subtly broken symmetry is beautiful makes it a thematic pattern that nature itself finds desirable to nurture and reproduce—again and again.

Tannic Acid

Tannic acid is made from nutgall, a swelling produced by parasitic wasps on oaks and other trees. Tannic acid itself is a light yellow powder that darkens when exposed to light. It has powerful astringent properties. When it is applied to the skin it forms insoluble crusts and hardens the skin below. It is used as an active ingredient in burn medicines, is combined with silver nitrate to remove tattoos, and has recently been found to heal fever blisters.

Tanning

In most pre-twentieth century Western cultures, pale skin was coveted as a sign of social status, reflecting leisure time spent indoors as opposed to hours passed outdoors working in the sun. Today this trend has reversed itself. Although an unfortunate lingering discrimination against persons of darker skin color remains in the United States, ironically, suntanned skin is now a means for asserting status. A tan can mean that a person has the time and money to take extended trips to fair-weather climates. However, in addition to being a reflection of financial stature, the newfound admiration for bronze skin is entangled with the increasing emphasis on physical health in this country. Recently, with the availability and low cost of tanning salons, the demarcation of wealth is somewhat blurred; a winter tan does not necessarily indicate indulgence in a tropical vacation.

Tanned skin is a natural by-product of the relatively new pastime of public, outdoor bathing. The bathing beauty who emerged in the twenties, along with the Miss America Pageant, meant an increase in the extent and kind of attention paid to the skin. Once it became socially acceptable to display large portions of skin in public, concern over its tone, texture, and color increased. The radiance of tanned and well-cared-for skin is also part of the look associated with bodybuilders, athletes in general, and most Hollywood stars to whom a healthy body is an essential professional tool.

Exposure to the sun activates the body's production of vitamin D. However, this positive process does not proceed indefinitely; too much sun invariably means one thing: too much sun. The only natural protection the skin has against the sun's harsh rays is the production of melanin. The capacity of the skin to produce melanin and, therefore, to tan is generally predetermined. The darker the skin, the less likely one is to have problems caused by the sun. Unfortunately, no one is completely safe. Extended exposure to ultraviolet rays results in undeniable damage to the skin, including premature aging and melanoma, or other types of skin cancer. Moderation and a great deal of preventive moisturizing should be rules for all sunbathers.

See also: SKIN, SUNBURN

Tattoos

Tattooing involves marking the body with punctures accentuated with pigmentation. "Tattoo" comes from the Tahitian word *tatta* meaning "to mark." Tattoos are a common form of personal adornment throughout primitive societies. Some rare carvings of the human form that date back 25,000 years to the late Stone Age bear geometric marks on the face and body that archaeologists believe signify tattoos. There is also some archaeological evidence to suggest that the ancient Egyptians and even men and women of the Ice Age indulged in the practice. Captain Cook brought the practice to the West, his sailors copying the South Sea islanders they encountered.

The motivation for tattooing varies from the highly spiritual to the defiant to the mundane. The most elaborate tattoos were developed by the Maori of New Zealand and by the Japanese, who completely clothed the body in highly detailed tattooing, creating a breathtaking sight. Over the ages, many institutionalized religious sects have forbidden tattoos. Tattooing is potentially unhealthy (unclean needles can transmit hepatitis and HIV). However, tattooing has been used by governments to record information about a person. The medical community has used the same procedure to "remove" birthmarks by injecting pigment to match natural skin tone.

At least 10 percent of the population of the United States has some form of tattoo. Over 50 percent of the population of British and American prisons has tattoos; researchers believe that this is an indication of a search for identity and—in the case of the superstitious—protection in dangerous, alienating situations.

Because the process of tattooing itself is somewhat painful—modern tattoos are created with electric needles—tattoos are associated in many masculine minds with bravery. If the popularity of this practice among the military men in the United States is any indication, these permanent emblems are generally metaphors for love, war, or a combination of the two. Tattoos provide a visual image of physical strength (such as daggers), pledges of devotion (initialized hearts), and even the conflict between the two (a pierced or bleeding heart). Perhaps tattooing is one of the clearest bridges between primitive and industrialized societies, representing in both a ritualistic mark of initiation.

See also: SELF-MUTILATION, SKIN

Teenagers

"When they reach the age of fifteen and their beauty arrives, it's very exciting—like coming into an inheritance."
—Eve Babitz, "The Sheik"

"Teen," a word with Greek and Sanskrit origins, means affliction, misery, and suffering. Most people would agree that this accurately describes at least a good portion of the years between the ages of eleven and eighteen. During these years, puberty—the time in the maturation process when sexual reproduction becomes physically possible—occurs. The body is thrown into a chaotic state of fluctuating hormones. Hormones have a powerful effect on a person's physical and mental condition. They control growth rate, and during the teen years a growth spurt of four to six inches per year is possible. Sufficient protein and vitamin intake is essential during this time for normal growth.

Typically, teenagers are simultaneously both negligent of and hyperbolically concerned about their health and appearance. Even though the human body can withstand a great deal of abuse, poor health habits developed during the teen years can impair potential longevity and physical appearance in the years which follow. At least 30 percent of eleven to fourteen-year-olds in the United States already have a high cholesterol level. Reportedly, 41 percent put salt on almost all food prepared at home; an excessively salty diet is the number one cause of high blood pressure. Nearly 60 percent of teenage girls fail to get any form of strenuous exercise. When the quick metabolism of a body being barraged by hormonal changes eventually slows to a normal adult rate, a poor diet and lack of exercise inevitably result in weight problems.

Ignorance about the nature of body chemistry can result in obesity and eating disorders with damaging psychological effects. Both smoking and drinking—activities often taken up in response to peer pressure without sufficient knowledge of their addictive properties—have direct negative effects on physical appearance also.

While many teens are excruciatingly concerned about how others see them, they fail to read accurate information about health, hygiene, and beauty and fall prey to beauty aids that make seductive promises of instant miracles. Weight loss is never instant without dieting and exercise, just as no cream can ever increase breast size. Products that make such promises should be examined suspiciously, for they may actually prove harmful.

The most common worry among teenagers is the appearance of their skin. The combination of a high level of hormonal activity and poor eating habits greatly increases the chances of developing acne during the teen years. This is also the age when many persons begin experimenting with cosmetics. Just as in primitive societies, this practice emblemizes a rite of passage to adulthood. In order to prevent the occurrence of severe acne that can leave scars that last a lifetime, teenagers should understand the relationship between skin, cosmetics, and pimples. Cosmetics do not cause pimples, but poor hygiene can.

See also: ACNE, SKIN

Teeth

Structure. The efficient structure of the teeth enables humans to break down food for digestion. The teeth are situated in the jaws. They are designed for chewing, biting, and tearing. Sharks are fortunate enough to have series after series of full sets of teeth. Humans are not quite so lucky; two sets are our limit. The primary set, or baby teeth, consists of twenty teeth. The second set has thirty-two. These sets are formed from pairs of teeth so that the left and right halves of the mouth form a mirror image. Most humans are born toothless (a few notable exceptions being Julius Caesar, Louis XIV, Napoleon, and Richard III). The teeth normally begin to appear between the ages of five and a half and ten months. The buds of permanent teeth appear six months after birth but do not push to the surface for six years.

Each tooth consists of a sensitive, vascular pulp surrounded by dentine—the hard, dense, bonelike tissue forming the body of a tooth under the coating of enamel that covers the crown—and a root that connects it to nerve endings. Enamel allows for the grinding and cutting of food. It is the hardest substance in the human body, made to last many years since, unlike the skin that covers the body, it cannot replace itself.

The basic shape of the tooth is a cone, with variations to accommodate the different functions the teeth perform. Incisors at the front and mid-mouth have a sharp, flattened crown and a wide edge; canines, at the corners of the mouth, have a sharp cusp; premolars are bicuspid, formed from two fused cones; and molars, the teeth which are largest and furthest back, consist of several cones fused to form a broad chewing surface.

Gentian

Sage

In developed societies, tooth decay has indeed been one of the great killers. (Very little evidence of tooth decay is found in the skulls of early or among primitive peoples.) The term for tooth decay, or dental caries, is derived from the Greek prefix *ker*, meaning death. Many doctors claim that more disease results from tooth or gum decay, caused by neglected teeth than from alcohol abuse. Theoretically, all children are born with equal potential for healthy, strong, well-formed teeth and gums, but the ravages of neglect can begin to take place early—even in utero if the mother's diet is poor. The high sugar content of much food ingested by the average American child plus inadequate brushing quickly reduce a child's initial potential for ideal, beautiful teeth. (The average American fifteen-year-old has eight cavities.) The good news is that cavities among elementary school children have dramatically declined since the sixties.

Although the tooth is the most likely structure in the body to perish during an individual's lifetime, it is the most resistant to decay after death. This is why the history of tooth decay has been documented so thoroughly: in addition to written accounts, the remains of human skeletons provide empirical evidence of its presence or absence in different cultures. In fact, much of history might have been different had more knowledge about dental care been available in the past. Many heads of state such as Louis XIV of France and Elizabeth I of England made important decisions while suffering from the agony of massive tooth decay. At least today the knowledge is readily available for those who seek it.

Unhealthy teeth are a liability by any standard. In ancient Rome, an article in the Law of the Twelve Tables states that "Whoever shall cause the tooth of a free man to be knocked out shall pay a fine of three hundred and that of a slave one hundred and fifty." Today, an individual human tooth is valued at $1,000 by most insurance companies; therefore, by monetary standards, the teeth merit a certain amount of care.

Teeth are important aesthetically, too. Unhealthy teeth can greatly mar an otherwise attractive face. Teeth in bad condition lead to self-consciousness and a fear of smiling or speaking freely. Oscar Wilde, a British playwright of the Victorian period renowned for his sarcastic wit, was thought to have a sour disposition because he rarely smiled and kept a hand in front of his mouth when speaking in public. In truth, decayed teeth had led him to acquire a set of ill-fitting false teeth of which he was ashamed. Even Vincent van Gogh, in a letter to his brother, Theo, expressed concern over the appearance of his teeth; he hoped that improving their appearance might help his career as an artist somehow.

Olive

Tooth Care. Dental practices of earlier times are interesting, though they were often ineffective or damaging. In times less knowledgeable about dental care, it was commonly believed that rubbing the teeth with the gentian plant, sage, or bark of peach, alder, or olive trees would prevent tooth decay, not to mention make the tongue more flexible, purge the blood of phlegm, and increase one's sexual potency. The earliest toothpastes, called tooth powders, were made from pulverized brick dust, salt, soot, perfumed water, vitriol, and, according to Erasmus, human urine.

In order to maintain an attractive smile, gums and teeth must be given regular and informed attention. Not only do flossing and brushing fight the germs that accumulate in the mouth, but they also provide the gums with essential exercise. However, brushing too forcefully pushes the gums back from the teeth, exposing the roots. The teeth should be brushed gently but thoroughly with a soft bristle brush, in a steady circular motion, at least twice daily after eating. Fluoride toothpastes have been proven extremely effective in fighting cavities. Fluoride combines with the enamel of the teeth, making it about 40 percent more resistant to decay. Since periodontal disease resulting from plaque buildup on the gums is the most common cause of tooth loss, dentists urge their patients to floss frequently in addition to brushing.

Another less devastating but physically blighting dental phenomenon is tooth discoloration. Too much caffeine in the diet and tobacco use leads to yellow teeth. The solution to stained teeth is not brushing more vigorously; this only scrapes away precious enamel. Reliable teeth polishers and brighteners are now available commercially, but they should never be used exclusively, as a substitute for toothpaste, if they lack fluoride. Also, any product that promises pure, white teeth is suspect for two reasons: first, it is a virtually impossible feat to accomplish; second, it is not necessarily desirable because teeth, like pearls, are not naturally snow white.

Cavities may very well become a thing of the past as an awareness of and access to methods for the maintenance of healthy teeth become commonplace. With the dissemination of knowledge about the importance of attentive dental care, an increase in the status associated with dental care products has occurred. Some specially designed toothbrushes are now available for purchase at prices as high as $99! Unfortunately, even as tooth decay is slowly being conquered in developed countries, dental health is worsening in Third World countries. It is hoped that dental care will spread to developing countries before their dental statistics ever rival those of the civilized West.

False Teeth.

> *"Glasco had none, but now some teeth has got;*
> *Which though they furre, will neither ake, or rot.*
> *Six teeth he has, whereof twice two are known*
> *Made of a Haft, that was a mutton-bone.*
> *Which not for use, but meerly for the sight,*
> *He wears all day, and draws those teeth at night."*
> —Robert Herrick (1591–1674), "Upon Glasco"

The manufacture of false teeth is almost as old as humanity. The first false teeth were invented by the Etruscans around 700 B.C. They were carved from bone or ivory taken from young cattle and held together by gold bands. Early false teeth were procured from animals, dead slaves, and battle victims. For centuries, false teeth were emblems of wealth or status. The embarrassment associated with false teeth did not emerge until the nineteenth century, corresponding with attempts to develop a more natural look. (This parallels the change in feelings from favoring elaborate periwigs to toupees.) As a matter of fact, false teeth were first created as a kind of jewelry, not as a means for chewing better. During the Puritan regime in England, false teeth were perceived as a mark of vanity. Those who had them seldom smiled and often developed the habit of concealing the mouth with one hand. Through the eighteenth century, provincial folk, too shy or poor to invest in a trip to the city, could order a crude set of teeth through the mail by sending a wax imprint of the mouth. Porcelain teeth were introduced in the United States in 1785 and George Washington was among the first to acquire some.

With the discovery of the rubber vulcanizing process by Charles Goodyear, it became possible to keep dentures in place. Today many people wear false teeth that are so natural looking it is difficult even for relatives to detect them. Dentists carefully photograph the natural teeth before removing the originals so that the color, size, and shape can be reproduced—blemishes and all if desired! But even with modern dentures, biting pressure in the mouth is reduced from 150 to 250 pounds per square inch to 10 to 30 pounds. Thus, it is important to protect the natural set of permanent teeth.

See also: LACTIC ACID

Theatrical Makeup

"Makeup and costume have an enormous significance and contribute half of the success, even for the most brilliant and talented actor."
—Konstantin Stanislavski

Makeup has long been a tool of the theater professional vital to the creation of a character. In the earliest theater of ancient Greece, performers wore masks. These masks were understood as significant, almost holy objects and were created and handled with reverential care. The appearance of the bare human face on stage occurred much later during the Middle Ages when the Catholic church began to sponsor passion plays composed around biblical themes. Even so, for centuries theatrical makeup was quite primitive. Performers had to make do with burnt cork and chalk until greasepaint was invented in the mid-eighteenth century in Germany. The use of cosmetics for the stage became gradually more refined as audience sophistication increased. Makeup at this time was very exaggerated since the limited visibility offered by gas lighting in theaters ruled out the possibility of subtlety. With the innovation of electric light in the late nineteenth century, more exposure made greater refinement worthwhile. This led to exploration of the use of shadowing and contouring of the face. Still, most actors simply reconstructed time-worn, clichéd makeup designs that made their characters little more than caricatures. Unlike their fellow thespians in the East, Western actors did not perceive makeup as an integral part of creating a role. (In the East, the ritualistic application of theatrical makeup is an ancient tradition.)

By the thirties when film had become firmly established as an art form in its own right, the motivation for a new attitude toward theatrical makeup emerged. Because magnified size of the projected movie, film wrought a dramatic change in the degree of care with which makeup was applied. Finally, it was understood in the West that the application of makeup for the stage and screen had to be perceived as an art, and that the person who designed such makeup needed a considerable amount of artistic sensibility in order to be successful. Film star Greer Garson is said to have remarked that the ideal makeup artist had to be a precise blend of sculptor, portrait painter, humorist, and curious student. In an interview about the nature of this field, Bill Tuttle, Oscar-winning makeup artist, encouraged young makeup artists to study drawing, painting, and sculpture as "all contribute to a basic knowledge that is necessary in any makeup process, be it simply beautification or characterization."

On stage or in film, a beautiful face does not always appear as such across the footlights. In order to produce the magnetism essential to maintain an audience's attention throughout the course of a drama, an actor must use his or her makeup as a precious tool. Good theatrical makeup shows careful attention to the demands of setting, circumstance, and character; it works to draw in—not close out—the viewer. It is guided by the attitude that the application of makeup is to be approached as an art, and with economy. These are valuable lessons even in nontheatrical realms.

Toner

See: ASTRINGENT

Toupee

Toupees are no longer the comical, ill-fitting, and unnatural constructions they once were. High-quality toupees are now custom-made and virtually undetectable, designed carefully to blend with one's natural hair. Because of the involved nature of the procedure, a custom-made toupee usually requires a full month to build. The cost is high, approximately $1,000. But for the man whose sense of self-worth is damaged by premature baldness, it may be a worthwhile investment. The act of wearing a toupee is no indication of depleted manhood if film actor Burt Reynolds is any example!

See also: HAIR PROBLEMS, WIGS

"Tummy Tuck" (Abdominal Lipectomy)

An abdominal lipectomy, commonly referred to as a tummy tuck, is cosmetic surgery to remove excess skin and fat, tighten loose stomach muscles, and, in some cases, repair hernias. Hernias are likely to be an issue only after multiple pregnancies or significant abdominal surgery. The results of this operation are a tightened and flattened abdomen, but the cost is a repositioned navel, some scarring, a hospital stay of several days, and postsurgical pain for several weeks. This surgery will not remove stretch marks unless they are located in the region of skin that will actually be cut out. The effects of the surgery are permanent unless a person gains a large amount of weight again and the skin is restretched. Therefore, it is advisable to consider this operation only after weight has stabilized.

See also: COSMETIC SURGERY

Underweight Problem

Some people are inordinately thin, to the point of being or feeling unhealthy. Many thin people are actually unaware of how little they eat; they skip meals without noticing. This can be an indication of high stress. Also, the blood circulation in a person under a great deal of stress is kept away from the digestive system because it is too busy concentrating on feeding the muscles. If the digestive system is not allowed to function properly, the appetite is curbed. Food often passes through without being assimilated, and nutritional benefits are lost.

Another common cause of excessive thinness is an overactive thyroid gland. In this case, eating sugar laden and fatty foods will only further stimulate the gland and worsen the problem. However, the activity of the thyroid gland usually slows with age, sometimes catching the chronically thin person unawares. This is why it is important to note what one is eating and how one's body responds throughout one's life.

The best means for combating thinness is to engage in exercise and relaxation before meals which will lower stress and stimulate the appetite. Those who are underweight do have several advantages. They tend to live longer, have better general health, and have an advantage in wearing today's fashions. Yet thinness, though valued by our culture, may be quite dangerous. Extremely underweight persons who insist that they are overweight may be suffering from anorexia nervosa.

See also: EATING DISORDERS

Venus

See: APHRODITE

Victorian Era

The Victorian era was characterized by a great deal of prudery and repression. It is named for the reign of Queen Victoria of England (1837–1901). Unhealthy attitudes toward the human body were apparent in the fashions as well as the art and politics of the time. "Bifurcated women" (or women in slacks) were considered obscene or immodest at best, and most women wore long, full skirts. It was even considered immodest to leave the legs of pianos and tables exposed! Women often ate their meals in seclusion to avoid unpleasantries at the dinner table resulting from problems with ill-fitting false teeth or overly corseted abdomens. This practice of dining alone also cultivated the illusion that young ladies lived on a diet of air.

This was a quiet time in the history of cosmetics. The use of cosmetics became associated largely with two fringe groups: the actor and the prostitute. The feminine blush, a symbol of modesty and purity, was supposed to occur naturally, although many women surreptitiously resorted to pinching their checks or applying rouge in secret. The only genuinely "acceptable" cosmetic was eau de cologne. However, there was a tremendous concern for cleanliness during this time, and nighttime beauty masks were used often to protect the skin.

Henry T. Finke, an early psychologist writing with obvious chauvinism in the nineteenth century, claimed that beauty, as a feature of evolution, had reached its pinnacle in the aristocratic English gentleman. Men during this time were allowed more free use of cosmetics. Almost every gentlemen at least used cologne and wore castor oil or beeswax to shape and promote the growth of his hair. The society at large, however, considered the ideal to be female, with a small, rosebud mouth, large, deep blue eyes, arched brows, deadly pale skin, abundant, but concealed hair, and a rigidly corseted figure. Cosmetics gradually became more acceptable as advertisers stressed their restorative properties and healthful qualities.

Virtue

"What is beautiful is good and who is good will soon be beautiful."
—Sappho

The association between beauty and goodness occurs quite naturally in all human cultures. This does not mean that all people automatically attribute goodness to that which is physically attractive; that would be too simplistic. Prettiness alone is not sufficient to be seen as virtuous. Instead, the relationship between beauty and virtue is cumulative and builds upon itself; not only does beauty have the potential to create good, but also goodness makes a thing or person beautiful.

As the Greek philosopher Plato describes in the *Symposium*, an appreciation of beautiful forms is only the first step toward understanding the essence of beauty. Recognizing physical beauty provides the initial fuel for the quest for fair practices and ideas. The virtuous aspect of beauty is not so much a quality as it is a process. We have faith in the long-range, transcendent power of beauty. This reflects the inherent optimism of human nature. Most human beings possess a firm belief that progress is possible. The presence of beauty in the natural world promotes the belief that more beauty is ultimately possible.

In this age of widely diversified cultures and rapid change, many respected intellectuals warn against an easy definition of progress. But progress has always been difficult to identify from within a system or a particular historical epoch; an event or idea can only be termed "progressive" after it has withstood the test of time. Yet even amid skepticism about what constitutes progress, the instinct that progress can be furthered, and that beauty is one of its chief tools, persists universally.

The connection among beauty, light, truth, and goodness has been reinforced in poetry, philosophical discourse, and even theology. Beauty is often connected with the notion of radiance or light. Entities as diverse as artwork, complexions, smiles, the setting sun, and heaven can all be described as "radiant." It is no accident that "Paradise" in Dante's *Divine Comedy* is infused with light, while his "Inferno" is characterized by darkness and stagnant air.

The relationship between beauty and truth is analogous to that between beauty and light. Among the most frequently cited statements on beauty is the creation of poet John Keats; in his "Ode to a Grecian Urn," he attributes the urn itself with saying,

> *"Beauty is truth, truth beauty,"—that is all*
> *Ye know on earth, and all ye need to know.*

American poet Emily Dickinson also expressed a belief in that relationship when she wrote,

> *I died for beauty, but was scarce*
> *Adjusted in the tomb*
> *When one who died for Truth was lain*
> *In an adjoining room.*

Beauty is understood as that toward which most of humanity is striving. Many scientists and thinkers believe that nature itself is perpetually working for more beautiful organization. This belief was expressed in the early twentieth century by English poet laureate Robert Bridges. In his sonnet entitled "The Growth of Love," he writes:

> *beauty being the best of all we know*
> *Sums up the unsearchable and secret aims of nature.*

But it is important to recognize that poets are not the only ones who attribute this power to beauty. George Santayana, a significant twentieth century philosopher, wrote this statement on the nature of beauty:

> *Beauty is a pledge of the possible conformity between the soul*
> *and nature, and consequently, a ground of faith in the*
> *supremacy of the good.*

Furthermore, Alfred North Whitehead, a philosopher and mathematician, in his book *Adventures of Ideas*, lists "beauty" as one of the five qualities essential to the definition of civilization along with truth, adventure, art, and peace. Except for anomalies like dadaism (a radical antiaesthetic movement of post–World War I Europe) and contemporary proponents of the "demystification" of art, most important thinkers in the East as well as the West have perceived the awareness of beauty as a noble and ennobling impulse.

Sufism, a branch of Islamic mysticism that originated in Persia, explains the attraction to beauty in the following way:

> Saints and kings, prophets and dervishes, all bow down before beauty, descending from the unknown world. We love beauty because it is not merely of this Earth, beauty in the human being as a reflection of celestial beauty itself (from *Secret Garden*, a thirteenth century Sufi text).

Beauty is virtuous because it is akin to the immortal:

> *A thing of beauty is a joy forever:*
> *Its loveliness increases; it will never*
> *Pass into nothingness; but still will keep*
> *A bower quiet for us, and a sleep*
> *Full of sweet dreams, and health, and quiet breathing,*
> —John Keats, *Endymion*

Beauty has survival value and, in a universe whose history is the story of the continual development of more numerous and more complex species with much sacrifice along the way, elements that promote the survival and proliferation of the most advanced entities are, by definition, good. Beauty inspires the will to persevere. And thus, in the words of poet and philosopher Ralph Waldo Emerson, beauty becomes "its own excuse for being" ("The Rhodora").

Vitamins

The human body needs only a thimblefull of the proper vitamins to function well. However, it is critical that they be in the proper balance. Each kind of vitamin meets a specific need, and no amount of one can compensate for the lack of another. Scientists have discovered at least twenty-five different vitamins essential to human health and development and speculate that further investigation will reveal many more. There are two distinct types of vitamins: water-soluble ones such as vitamins C and B-complex, and fat-soluble ones, such as vitamins A, D, and E.

The realization that diseases such as rickets and scurvy are the result of a vitamin deficiency is relatively new. But the increased awareness of the value of vitamins has generated a new kind of ignorance. No amount of vitamin C will eliminate a common cold. Vitamins are not miracle workers and, as with anything, too much of a good thing can be harmful; an excessive intake of vitamins can even be toxic.

See also: NUTRITION

Wigs

The practice of wearing wigs dates back to the earliest recorded time. Assyrians, Phoenicians, Greeks, and Romans all used hairpieces of some kind. The Egyptian pharaohs and their royal families would pluck their entire heads and don long wigs of spiraling curls made from human hair, palm-leaf fibers, or wool. The wigs of ancient Rome were crimped, frizzed, and decorated with jewels, flowers, and ribbons. For many primitive cultures, including the Australian Aborigines, wig making is a highly involved art form.

The enormous wigs of the Aborigines, which are made of human hair, are mounted on bamboo frames. They are worn only by men. The persons who design and construct them are specially selected. They undergo a rigorous, secret training during which time (as well as during any time a wig is actually being made) the makers of the wigs must refrain from sexual intercourse. A pig must be sacrificed before each individual wig is crafted. Upon completion, a wig is presented to a man in a ceremony that commemorates his maturation.

Mary Stuart, while imprisoned by Elizabeth I, changed her wig every day in order to have something to do. But in the sixteenth century, the wearing of wigs was generally limited to those wishing to compensate for natural flaws. For example, as Queen Elizabeth, never known for an abundance of hair, began to age and her baldness increased, she donned a wig. By the seventeenth century, everyone who was anyone wore a wig. The first elaborate wigs are associated with the likes of Marie Antoinette, Madame de Pompadour (for whom a particular hairstyle is named), and British barristers. The average fashionable man began wearing wigs in 1660, and during this time, most of the finer homes were equipped with a special "powder closet" to which guests could retire to replenish powder on hair or wig. American colonists were rationed one pound of flour per week to use as hair powder during this period of elaborate wigs. Many noblewomen had to hire a special maid trained in the art of maintaining these elaborate hairpieces made from wire, fabric, and human hair. Regrettably, the human hair used in making wigs was often acquired from smallpox and distemper victims which caused the spread of these diseases.

The first wig colors were light brown, blue, and pale gray. The black wig became fashionable in 1670 and remained so in the colonies until the turn of the century. White, pink, and violet wigs were introduced in 1703. Gray was worn exclusively for mourning.

The ornate designs with which these wigs were sculpted required that the wig be lacquered to the head with starch, a process which took easily two hours. Because of the involved nature of this procedure, women wore these wigs around the clock for three to nine weeks in the summer, and for a slightly shorter period in the winter. At the end of this time, a "cutting out" procedure was enacted. Vermin which had moved in were exterminated.

Following the American and French revolutions, the wig experienced a decline due to its association with elevated social status. In the eighteenth century, wigs were worn only surreptitiously and by women. In the twentieth century, due to the development of synthetic hair, the wearing of wigs became democratized. In the Orient, wigs have only been worn as costume pieces in the theater, probably because baldness is extremely rare among Orientals.

See also: TOUPEE

Wrinkles

Wrinkles occur when the fatty support underlying the surface of facial skin dissipates, leading to a decrease in the elasticity of the face. When the layer of fatty tissue shrinks, the skin sags. Wrinkles generally form at right angles to muscles.

Because of the association of beauty with youth, most people try to minimize their wrinkles. In the nineteenth century, the duchess of Newcastle developed what she claimed to be a "cure" for wrinkles as well as age spots. It was made from oil of vitriol (sulfuric acid) and applied to the skin. The idea was that in removing the top layer of skin the clear, smooth skin below would be revealed! Far more effective (not to mention safer) antiaging creams are now available on the market. These products contain substances such as mink oil which may soften and lubricate the skin. Firming gels for the area below the eyes are also available which promise to minimize the development of future dry lines.

It is possible to take steps to prevent the early or excessive development of wrinkles, but only cosmetic surgery can eliminate existing wrinkles. One of the best preventives is staying out of the sun and using facial moisturizers daily after cleansing the skin. Also, mentally take note of the facial muscles during the course of the day and try to avoid unconscious facial mannerisms such as frowning, furrowing the brow when concentrating, squinting, and scrunching up the nose. A fluid, expressive face is a wonderful thing, but the habit of locking the face into static poses can lead to early or exaggerated wrinkles. These habits are usually the result of tension carried in the face. Self-massage, in addition to increased self-awareness, can effectively break these wrinkle-forming habits.

See also: SKIN

𝒴

𝒴𝑜𝑔𝑎

Yoga, a system of mental and physical exercise and relaxation, originated in the East. "Yoga" actually means "integration." As a discipline, it is designed to promote holistic beauty—through the centered union of an individual's physical, spiritual, emotional, and intellectual components. Yoga provides an ideal means for counterbalancing a fast-paced life-style. This may be one reason why it experienced a major surge in popularity in the West in the sixties and seventies. Yoga continues quietly to attract new practitioners today, including many Hollywood stars.

The goal of yoga is internal balance attained through the physical self. Many psychologists assert that habitual thought patterns and chronic tensions are manifested in the body. Any ingrained physical patterns, particularly when they are unconscious, are detrimental to a person's appearance. Yoga provides a way to break these patterns down in addition to firming the muscles and acquiring greater poise and flexibility.

Technically speaking, yoga involves a series of controlled, slow movements toward various formalized positions. Some positions, such as the lotus, are initially quite painful. The idea behind yoga is to confront the pain without force—to simply exist through it—until it disappears. Acceptance of the discomfort, through concerted concentration, produces a clear head and a stronger, freer body.

Most practitioners strongly recommend that anyone who is seriously interested in exploring the craft of yoga first acquire a good teacher.

Some of the benefits of yoga include:

- greater breath control and capacity
- stronger immune system
- improved figure and posture
- increased concentration
- better coordination
- mental clarity
- radiance
- stress management
- freedom from unwanted habits

Zinc Oxide

Zinc oxide is a dense white powder made by burning coal with zinc carbonate in a special furnace. It is used as a dusting powder or ointment for some skin conditions. It can be used to cover skin blemishes such as freckles. Unlike bleach, it appears to eliminate irregular pigmentation by adhering to the darkened skin. Zinc oxide is an ingredient in acne treatments, rouge, and sunburn lotions.